RIVERFLOW

by

Alison Layland

HONNO MODERN FICTION

First published in 2019 by Honno Press, 'Ailsa Craig', Heol y Cawl,
Dinas Powys, Vale of Glamorgan, Wales, CF64 4AH

1 2 3 4 5 6 7 8 9 10

A catalogue record for this book is available from the British Library.

Published with the financial support of the Welsh Books Council.

ISBN 978-1-909983-97-7 (paperback)
ISBN 978-1-909983-98-4 (ebook)

Cover design: Graham Preston
Text design: Elaine Sharples
Printed in Wales by Gomer Press

21st October 1998

So Bede and I finally met. And now the initial joy's faded, I'm seriously wishing he'd never made that call, wishing he'd vanish from my life.

Joe snapped the diary shut. Every so often he'd retrieve it and pour out his thoughts, but as far as he could remember this was the first time he'd actually read back over anything he'd written. After all these years, such negativity was hard to recall now that Bede was more like a son than a nephew, Elin a daughter-in-law.

This was no time to wallow in memories; he was here for a purpose. Once again aware of the wild wind and the rain like a horde of devils dancing on the roof, he picked up the metal box and stuffed the battered book back into it. The hollow creaks of the workshop surrounded him, part familiar, part warning, water dripping noisily from the dormant waterwheel. He glanced around in the semi-darkness, then climbed the wooden ladder to the platform in the rafters and negotiated the intricacies of shafts and belts towards the hidden hollow between heavy roof timbers and wall. He'd noted the spot ages ago, when they were rebuilding the place. No one knew there was anything to look for, and if they ever did, it would be safely concealed here. Safe and dry.

Maybe Bede and Elin had been right: maybe there was no need to move anything, and his time would have been better spent in the village, with them, helping others prepare for the flood. But just as he had done in the house, he felt an urgent need to get their most precious things higher, out of reach of water. The dancing devils on the roof slates, along with the ever-present roar of the leat outside, made him feel vindicated. Their renovations to the mill race had not been truly tested yet; the water could easily break out and inundate their house and smallholding. Bede put too much faith in his calculations, trying to convince Joe that, unlike the swollen river running through the fields below, it would stay put. His nephew had a sense of justice, as though the rightness of their way of life meant it was only fair they wouldn't be flooded here. But Joe knew that life wasn't fair.

He stowed the box away then wavered. Tempted to dive back into the past, he reached out, but a rustle in the workshop below checked him.

'Hello? Back already?'

No reply. There were probably rats seeking shelter from the deluge too. The moment broken, he quickly descended the ladder, padded over to the door and put his boots back on.

Hunching against the daggers of cold and wet, he paused for a moment in the scant shelter of the doorway to lock up and pull his hat down securely. The lowering clouds and water-saturated air had brought dusk on early. Late afternoon, and already it felt like time to go back into the house, draw the curtains and turn in on himself. He dashed across the yard, water streaming down his collar. Home and dry in the kitchen, he shook the worst of the wet from his jacket and petted his dog, who came running through from the living room to greet him. After a perfunctory welcome, Kip went to stand by the door, whining. Damn. He'd kept the dog in – these weren't conditions for him to go wandering – but there was no arguing with a call of nature.

He lit a cigarette and huddled in the porch as Kip nosed around the yard. Gazing down over the floodplain field across the road, now their willow plantation, he saw a regular flicker of motion: the river. It was more or less the highest he'd seen in all the years he'd lived here, so he scribbled Bede and Elin a quick note before following the dog down to the gate for a better view of the spectacle. No longer the benign friend of summer, the river was a restless dragon slithering its way past with a cargo of debris – logs dwarfed to the appearance of matchsticks, what looked like a caravan wall and a range of incongruous domestic items. He briefly wondered how the larger flotsam had got through the arch of the bridge, and what else had caught upstream of it. He doubted it would be long before the inevitable flood swallowed the bridge and most of Foxover High Street.

Joe had always found the river more alluring than threatening and, safe in the knowledge his wet clothes would soon be steaming in front of the fire, he called the dog, crossed the road and slipped through the lower field gate, stopping at a safe distance to watch the elemental power of the water.

Above the rumbling of rain and river, he became aware of Kip barking. He looked round and jumped as he saw someone swing open the gate and walk towards him. Probably some poor soul lost on the lanes. Hardly surprising on a day like this. He waved, grabbed the dog's collar and approached to see if there was anything he could do. Maybe he'd get credit for being of some use today, after all. The newcomer bent to the dog, who fell quiet, then straightened with a hint of a smile. Joe nodded back.

'Can I help you?'

'I think you can, Joe.'

Jolted, he narrowed his eyes. The voice, slightly raised above the noise of water, had a hint of something he recognised. He could see little of the face in the grey late-afternoon light, but it was enough.

'You can't keep me away by simply denying me,' the half-familiar voice said, and Joe realised he'd been shaking his head. 'Not any more.'

The shop was going to be inundated. No doubt about it. The rain, here and further west in the Welsh mountains, was as heavy as ever, the water rising, and Elin imagined the new ponds already dotted around the fields expanding to form lakes, inland seas. Already close to the highest of the ancient marks on the pub wall, the flood was soon going to lap at the doors of the community shop, and worse. As if to confirm it, the lights went out. Everyone else had long since gone home and in the weird glow of the emergency exit light, the shelves and display tables looked post-apocalyptic. At least it was a planned, damage-limitation desolation. Most of the Foxover Storehouse stock had been moved upstairs to the crammed store-room, the rest shared out among the boots of their cars. The high street was bustling with more activity than a Saturday morning as people rescued what they could, piling up futile-looking sandbags and checking flood defence barriers.

She tried Bede's mobile. No reply – typical. He'd been called away to the pub down by the river; she assumed he was still there. She texted Joe telling him not to bother coming – too bloody late now, but couched in concern for his safety, of course – before locking up the shop, pulling her hood over her ears and heading out into the street.

Battered by the deluge, she hurried to meet up with Bede and leave before the river cut off the bridge and forced them to drive miles out of their way to get home. From the pub porch, she felt the turbulent water ominously close. The arch of the bridge, normally sturdy and solid, looked like an empty gesture, a symbol of people's insignificance to the river. She suppressed the guilt she felt at actually liking the thought.

Inside the Horseshoes, always first hit when the waters rose, the lounge bar was spiky with chairs upended on tables – probably pointless, as the lot might soon be floating. She made her way in the half-light towards sounds of activity in the kitchen. Angie looked worn out, her usual good cheer subdued. They exchanged smiles of sympathy and encouragement.

'Bede here?'

'He's upstairs in the flat with Brian, sorting out the generator. He's been a star. Or will be, if he gets it going. Grab this and take it upstairs, will you, Elin love? I'll be right behind you, then we'll be ready to pull up the drawbridge.'

Her back aching, Elin took the box of food. As she reached the top of the stairs a sputtering engine noise accompanied the lights flickering on, off, then permanently on as the mechanical hum steadied.

'Yesss!' Bede's triumphant voice filled her with relief. No way would she have got him out and back to their car had it meant leaving a challenge unmet. She put the box down and turned.

'When all this is over, I'll sort you out with a proper solution,' Bede said to Brian as he tucked his glasses case in his pocket.

'You what?' The irritation in the landlord's voice seemed to pass her husband by.

'You've got a massive south-facing roof and—'

'Can't see solar panels doing much good on a day like today.'

'It's all about storage, mate. Get you set up with a battery. Anyway—'

'Yes, anyway,' Elin cut in. 'It's rising like crazy out there and we ought to be thinking about escaping.'

'I really appreciate your help,' Brian said. 'Though you can save the hard sell for another time.' He was only half-joking. 'I'm surprised you haven't told us how we deserve this.'

Elin winced. Bede paused in his search for his coat. 'I'm sorry?'

'Brought it on ourselves. Consumption. Pollution.'

Slowly and deliberately, Bede took his socks from in front of the fire, the way he handled them indicating they were warm but still soaking, wrinkled his nose as he pulled them on and eased his feet into sodden boots. He stood and began buttoning his coat.

'This river has always flooded,' he said calmly. 'Throughout history. People have always dealt with it by pulling together.' He stood back to let Angie past with an armful of linen. 'Of course, the havoc we're wreaking on the climate means it'll happen more often, more forcefully from now on. But that doesn't mean…'

He smiled, leaving the several possibilities of what it didn't mean hanging in the air. Elin knew the main one would be '…that I'm quite such a tactless bastard.' She also knew from Brian's expression, and the half-bottle of whisky he proffered as they were leaving, that he realised it, too.

As they crossed the bridge, the overfull river felt strangely close. A muddle of debris jostled the upstream side. On their way home along the lane, Bede untied and shook out his hair before peering out of the side window.

'Wow, look at that. It's a lake out there.'

She stopped the car. Peering through the rain-streaked windows, she twisted to look back at the stranded bridge, its hump like a prehistoric creature wallowing between the woods on their side and Foxover on the far bank. The water had spread to the fields between river and road, and was continuing its ominous swell. In the rain-darkened late afternoon, they could just make out the other side, murky water lapping its way up the village street.

It was a relief to get home and turn into the Alderleat gate.

'I hope Joe's got a fire going,' Bede said as they hugged their coats around them ready to make a dash for the house.

He held the porch door open for her, but Elin paused on the threshold. She thought she heard the dog barking. It was hard to tell through the wind and rain, but it sounded like it was coming from the field by the river.

'Isn't that Kip?'

Bede called a hello into the house, listened for a moment, peered out alongside her. The barking was more distinct this time. They ventured back into the rain and hurried down to the yard entrance. The gate across the road was swinging open and Kip came through, bounding towards them. Frowning, she bent to him. Kip shook his sodden coat, sending out a shower of drops to blend with the rain.

'What's he doing here? Where's Joe?'

Without replying, Bede ran across the road and paused at the gate.

'I can't believe how high it's got since we left earlier.'

She joined him and saw that the water was fast lapping its way up the young trees of the willow plantation. He grabbed her arm and pointed into the branches to their left.

'What's that? I saw something move.'

Elin didn't look, because her eye was caught by a flash of silver straight ahead, down by the waterline. The distinctive V on the back of Joe's jacket. She brushed the rain from her face, horrified to see him being dragged out by a tug of the current towards a large branch that was sweeping by. Joe made no attempt to grab it, swim or even struggle.

'Bede! Over there!'

He swore and broke free from her, vaulting the fence between their field and the next, sprinting downstream, trying to keep up with the riverflow. There was clearly no hope of matching the speed of the current. She followed. At the far end of the field he reached the thick hedge and stopped at the water's edge. She had a horrible feeling he was about to dive in.

'Stop! Don't do anything stupid!'

She caught hold of him and they stood, helpless, as Joe and the branch were swept out of sight around the bend. Time was suspended for a frozen, drenched moment, before panic sent them both running to the house to get help.

No need for words

Eighteen months later

The little nests of light sailed downstream, flickering flames weaving fire patterns into the grey-brown tapestry of the evening current. Thirty-six miniature boats drifted off to merge with the orange streaks of fading sunset. And onwards, gradually moving out of sight round the lazy curve of the river, to fade, to burn out. Maybe to give unexpected pleasure to someone else along the way. Maybe not. This was theirs. If someone else happened to share it, that was fine.

Elin snuggled into the embrace of Bede's arm gently draped on her shoulder.

'Thank you.'

'Happy birthday,' he murmured.

It was a remarkable gift to celebrate the unremarkable thirty-six. Sometimes he'd simply give her a present. Sometimes it was different, a random flight of fancy. He was certainly more a man of gestures than things. She recalled her initial shock, some seventeen years ago, when he'd revealed the tattoo, his sign of commitment to their future life. She now reached up and gently traced the inked leaves showing in the open neck of his shirt, visualising the green-man-garlanded body art that delicately twined across his shoulders, leaves drifting to waters that meandered down his back like a seamless extension of his long, sandy-coloured hair. He raised her hand to his lips and kissed it.

The wind rustled the willow leaves of their plantation behind them. She looked again at the steadily vanishing lanterns. Like their miniature voyage, it hadn't been a smooth or easy ride. For the past year and a half, he'd hardly given her anything. She understood, but it was good to have him back. Leaning over, her hand on the cool grass, she looked around at their friends. Fran smiled.

'Happy birthday, Elin.'

She moved to give her a hug. Jeff did likewise. Fran exchanged conspiratorial glances with Bede; Elin now knew why, for the last few days, her friend had periodically vanished to the inner sanctum of the workshop. Elin had been busy with spring planting, and the atmosphere of contentment that had recently settled over Alderleat had soon turned any pangs of jealousy or exclusion into the anticipation of surprise. So now she knew: Fran had been helping Bede weave miniature baskets from scraps of withies.

As the last of the little boats bobbed from view, Kip came panting back along the bank, tail waving like a banner. He'd set off in fascination after the lanterns, trailing them as far as the hedgerow in the next field, and now his return was zigzagged by the distraction of evening scents in the undergrowth. Bede called him and ruffled the dog's mongrel brown fur as he settled at his feet.

'He says we've had enough of this inactivity,' he announced. 'And I'm inclined to agree. Night hike, anyone?'

Jeff rolled his eyes. 'Can't we just—'

'I'm up for it,' Fran said, deliberately ignoring her husband's help-me-out-here eyes. Elin smiled to herself. She was well aware that Jeff tolerated these occasional forays into country living for the sake of Fran's and her friendship.

Their current visit was nearly over and, after a week of fresh air and activity, Elin could almost feel the couch beckoning him across the gently-sloping water meadow. There was nothing she fancied more than heading for the open country beyond the house, but that was countered by the prospect of dragging a reluctant Jeff along, or leaving him behind and forcing Fran to make an awkward decision.

'How about a compromise?' she said, throwing a rope to a drowning man. 'What about a walk, but we make it pubwards? I could fancy a birthday drink.'

She looked at Bede, who nodded. It was hard to tell whether his smile was forced or genuine, but when he released Kip to run off after some enticing rustle in the willows, the dog's burst of energy felt like a statement.

'Sounds good to me,' Jeff said, his voice full of gratitude. 'Should be far enough even for Action Man to work up a thirst.'

'Sure.' Bede stood and began to gather up their things. 'I just thought it's a nice night and you two aren't here much longer. But the Horseshoes is fine by me. C'mon, birthday girl.'

He reached out and helped Elin to her feet. As Fran and Jeff set off, she hung back, allowing them to go ahead. The river was now sleek and dark. She and Bede gazed at the serpentine current for a moment, no need for words, before turning and walking up the gently sloping swathe of grassland between the willows and their boundary.

Kip caught up with them as they passed a stand of the alders that gave their name to the house and smallholding. Alderleat had been their home for almost fifteen years – for the last couple, since Joe's death, theirs alone. They crossed the lane to the house that beckoned with its ancient patchwork of brick and stone-built walls, its arched black eyebrows above the windows. The turbine stood guard on the hill beyond and the waterwheel waited in readiness, invisible but equally present, at the side of the workshop.

By the time they'd dumped the picnic things and gathered jumpers and jackets, Kip had settled on his favourite chair. Elin was relieved. Joe had been accustomed to taking his dog everywhere, including the pub, but Kip's in-your-face inquisitiveness didn't suit everyone, and home was the probably the best place for him on a busy Friday night.

As they walked down the lane towards Foxover, Bede drank in the scent of foliage hanging in the dusky air. The spring growth was almost tangible on warm nights like these. The leaves of the willows whispered to their right, along with the gentle sound of the river beyond, and a faint tang of sheep drifted towards him from Frank Barnham's fields to the left. Heightened by the darkening night air, soft sounds floated towards them from the village over the background murmur: a car in the distance, a door banging, a hint of voices.

He looked at Elin, wondering how to share the simple elation the evening air gave him. Can you feel the shoots growing too? Doesn't it make you feel…?

She smiled before he'd found a way to express it. The meeting of their eyes heightened the shared feeling where words would have reduced it to banality. He glanced back over his shoulder; even Jeff seemed moved to a listening silence. Or maybe his mind was simply on getting to the pub and sinking a couple of pints.

Come on, less of the negativity. What's actually wrong with the guy?

Bede tensed; Joe could still catch him unawares every now and then. Strange, he'd been sitting on the riverbank, the very place, for the last hour and not felt a thing. There was no logic. He should have spoken his green-shoot thoughts out loud to Elin, kept his mind on what really mattered. He'd got good at it; just sometimes… He reached for her hand.

Around the bend in the lane, they passed beneath the shadowy trees of Holtwood. The evening breeze rustled in the leaves, carrying the sounds of an extended family of rooks settling for the night, their busy cawing interspersed with the intrusive hollow *chak* of distant pheasants.

He could sense Elin's annoyance at the reminder of Philip Northcote's expanding shoot, and the far more ominous threat of the potential fracking site hovering over the fields beyond the woods. He squeezed her hand but said nothing, unwilling to contaminate her birthday evening.

The sound of a car on the bridge and the dazzle of approaching headlights caused them to step aside onto the verge as it passed, before walking on. They now had a clear view of the road all the way to the ancient stone bridge, and spread out to walk four abreast. The two women were in the middle and Bede glanced across, as ever struck by the way Fran's auburn, pre-Raphaelite dreaminess complemented Elin's short, dark elfin practicality. He'd always envied them their friendship.

'I can't believe it's our last full day tomorrow,' Fran said.

'Anything special you want to do?' Elin asked.

Fran gestured towards the trees. 'Didn't you say you needed to collect some timber?'

'You want to work on your last day?'

'Yeah, Fran,' Jeff cut in. 'I'm not sure—'

'It'd be great,' Fran insisted. 'Change is as good as a rest.

Especially if… Do you think the river's low enough for us to do it by making rafts? It used to be the highlight of our visits. Remember that time when…'

She fell silent. It had been Joe's idea to make hard work fun by bringing the logs home on the water instead of taking the tractor and trailer. Bede took a deep breath and surprised himself with how easily the words came out.

'Yeah, I think it should be fine. Great idea. Haven't done that for a while.'

He hoped the actions would come as easily as the words. Elin shot him a look of relief mixed with concern. 'You sure?'

Jeff waved a hand dismissively. 'I really don't—'

'Perfectly sure,' Bede said. 'We'll check it out in daylight tomorrow, but I don't see why not.'

Jeff continued to grumble and Bede left the women to work their charm on him as they crossed the bridge. In the riverside pub car park, he noticed Carole Denman's 4x4. He knew better than to make his customary remark about either its excessive size or the fact that she lived within walking distance; tact was the order of the day around Carole since the Frack-Free Foxover group had come together. Despite their differences, she and Elin had become friends, united by the campaign, with Carole even joining the community shop cooperative. Bede only wished, for Elin's sake more than his own, that he didn't always sense a spark of antagonism from the woman. As they entered the lounge bar, Carole had her coat on ready to leave. Elin thanked her for the birthday card and flowers she'd sent.

'We're here for a birthday drink,' Bede said. 'You fancy joining us?'

'Thanks, but I only called to see Angie. I ought to be… I've got such a busy day tomorrow.' She made a show of looking at her watch and smiling at Elin. 'Oh, go on, then. A quickie, seeing as it's you.'

Doubtless if it had been Elin who'd asked, she wouldn't have hesitated. He shrugged it off and a few minutes later was glad to get a warmer welcome from Brian behind the bar. The Horseshoes had its usual Friday-night buzz, a lively crowd of familiar faces mixed with visitors enjoying a drive out.

'Elin's birthday, eh?' The landlord looked over to where she and the others were settling at a table near the large inglenook fireplace. 'This round's on me.'

'Cheers, mate.' Bede grinned. 'Anyone would think you were after something.'

'Can't a man have a flush of generosity in his own pub?' Brian winked as he put an elderflower pressé on the bar with the rest of the drinks. Bede registered that he hadn't noticed Fran with a glass of beer or wine all the time they'd been here. He made a mental note to ask Elin about it.

A guitar struck up from the far corner. He looked over to see Gareth, one of the music-night stalwarts, and a lad in his early-to-mid twenties he'd seen around over the last few days.

'You squeezing in extra music sessions on a Friday now?' he asked Brian.

'Gareth got talking to Silvan there the other day and they asked if I minded them practising here. You know me, I'd have 'em in every night if they were willing.'

It was the perfect accompaniment to the chatter of a busy pub. Bede gathered three of the drinks between his hands and carried them over to the table.

'Back in a sec.' He went over to the musicians on his way to fetch the remaining drinks, hoping Elin wouldn't notice as he swerved around a group of people standing by the bar.

Gareth looked up as he approached.

'Hello, Eco,' he said, pausing in his playing.

'Evening. I wondered…could you give us some kind of birthday song?' He gestured back towards their table. 'For Elin.'

'Sure. We can think of something, can't we?' He looked at the other guy with his spiky black hair, ear full of studs and T-shirt proclaiming No Surrender, who was ostentatiously absorbed in bringing a complicated passage to a close. He could certainly play, and Bede said so.

'Thanks.' The young lad's fingers paused and he glanced up at last. 'Request, did I hear?' He wrinkled his nose. 'I'm not into rousing choruses of "Happy Birthday".'

His accent was local Shropshire, unlike Bede's northern or Elin's Welsh. Probably not a visitor, then, though he was new to the Horseshoes. He looked like he could be interesting to get to know.

'Me neither, mate, me neither,' Bede said. 'One of Elin's favourites will be fine. You know what she likes, don't you, Gareth?'

Gareth nodded. 'Have you two met?' He performed a flourishing wave of his arm. 'Silvan – Eco.'

'Bede Sherwell.' He offered his hand. The young man had a firm handshake and this time looked at him directly.

'Silvan Bewlay.' He fingered a leather friendship bracelet at his wrist. 'Bead? As in jewellery?'

'No, as in Venerable.'

'You what?'

'The eighth-century monk, later sainted. Famous for his *Ecclesiastical History of the English People* – the Anglo-Saxons, that is.'

'Whoa, listen to you! You some kind of historian?'

'Nope. Mechanic with an enquiring mind.' He was

reminded of why he'd begun his first term at high school as Ben. The experiment only lasted a few weeks; it soon became evident that it took more than a name to gain peer acceptance. 'You grow up with an unusual name, you want to find out about it.'

'If you say so. So your folks were historians,' Silvan persisted.

'Sorry to disappoint. My mum once told me she was captivated by a programme – Open University or some such – in the small hours during a night of pregnancy-induced insomnia. Said she hoped the name might endow me with some of that quiet, calm wisdom – something neither she, my father nor anyone else in the family seemed blessed with.'

It was probably the only clue she had ever given him to his father's identity: a man not blessed with quiet, calm wisdom. That narrowed it down.

'So what's your excuse? I bet you were the only Silvan in your class.'

'Never thought about it. A whim of my folks, I guess.' He strummed a casual chord. 'Didn't he just call you "Eco"? What's that about?'

Gareth laughed. 'Spend long enough in his company and you'll find out. You're lucky he hasn't given you a lecture already.'

'Oh, I usually save the lecture till at least the second meeting.' Bede winked. 'I'll spare you this time – I'd better be getting back to the birthday girl. Nice to meet you, mate. Enjoying the music, thanks.'

He collected the remaining drinks from the bar and went back to their table. Fran reached out melodramatically for her drink.

'Where d'you get to? I'm dying of thirst here.'

'Sorry.' He waved an arm vaguely across the busy room. 'Got a bit waylaid. Needed a word with Gareth about the pool team.'

Elin smiled and patted a stool beside her own. He wondered how her expression could so fluently convey that she knew perfectly well what he'd been up to but wasn't about to spoil his surprise. 'Is the music going to be a regular Friday thing?' she said. 'I'll bring my guitar next time.'

'Nothing official, but I'm sure they'd welcome you.'

'Who's the new fella?' Carole asked. Didn't we see him the other day in the shop?'

'He's called Silvan.'

'Has he moved to Foxover?' Elin asked.

'Possibly. Judging by his accent he's from somewhere round here. He didn't say and I never thought to ask.'

'You're hopeless.' Elin rolled her eyes and exchanged a look with Fran. 'Interesting young ace guitarist comes to the Horseshoes and he can't be arsed finding out who he is.'

'I'll try and do better next time, Mrs Sherwell.'

Elin ran her hand through his hair and kissed him. 'You've done well enough for me today. I was just telling Carole about your wonderful birthday present.'

'It sounds quite something,' Carole said. 'Really imaginative.'

'No need to sound surprised,' Bede replied and smiled in a vain attempt to cancel out his tone of voice. 'I have my moments.'

'If anyone else had done something like that you'd probably have regaled them about a frivolous waste of resources.' Carole glanced apologetically at Elin. Rather than take offence, Bede simply felt glad he didn't have a monopoly on tactless remarks.

'It was anything but waste,' he said calmly. 'A classic case of "upcycling".' His fingers formed air quotes in disdain for a trendy term to describe something they did as a matter of course, and he was relieved to see Elin's look of amusement. 'But in any case, creating something beautiful to make my wife happy is not what I'd call a frivolous waste.'

Elin stepped in. 'And I really appreciate it. I'm sure Carole didn't mean to criticise you.'

'Wouldn't dream of it,' she said.

Bede was saved from having to think of a reply by Gareth calling for hush and announcing a song for Elin's birthday.

21st October 1998

It all started a few weeks ago with the phone call. That voice, out of the blue – almost a man's, newly broken as if he didn't yet know what to do with the depth of it. Would've struggled to know what to say in any voice, I guess, and I can hardly blame him.

'Joe?' he says. 'Joe Sherwell?'

I confess I was a bit short with him. It had been a bad day in the shop and I'd had enough of talking to people.

He goes on, 'It's Bede here' or some such, and I replied 'Come again?'

He repeats it, his tone giving it, how many guys called Bede do you know?, and my silence saying just as eloquently, none. 'You know, Lydia's son.'

'Lydia?'

Lydia I know, of course, despite the years of estrangement. Son, I don't.

'Your sister, yeah? I have got the right number, haven't I?'

And it begins to dawn on me and I go 'Aye, sorry mate, I just wasn't expecting this', or something like that, and he gives it, 'She told me to call but it's obviously not the right thing to do after all, sorry to bother you, I'll leave you in peace.'

That got me to panicking and I more or less yelled at him to stay on the line.

And he told me she was dying.

It was just so weird a fortnight ago, seeing him there,

a real live fifteen-year-old, so soon after making my peace with our Lydia. I didn't go to the funeral, wasn't hard to keep my distance for the benefit of everyone concerned, but he kept me a handful of her ashes – he may be an awkward sod but seems his heart's a good 'un – and we took them and offered them up to the wind on Birkland Hill, said he needed his own space with his mum, too, away from 'them'. Jesus Christ, do I need someone else's baggage on top of my own! But seems she told him I'd be a mate so I'd better try and do the right thing this time.

Anyway, what with my sister's unexpected reappearance and equally unexpected (to me) death, finally seeing her boy and putting a reality to him, it must all be showing on the surface despite my best efforts, and Suzie starts on at me, asking what's up. Of course the subject of our Lydia and all that happened has always been a no-go area, so I manage to brush the inquisition off and hope it'll pass. Then she gets convinced I'm having an affair. Won't let it go, says she knows me too well.

Not that well. But even if it's no bloody affair, there's still all this stuff bubbling back to the surface that I clearly don't have a hope in hell of hiding, let alone dealing with. Niggle, niggle, niggle. Two weeks of it till I got back from my last fishing trip to find her threatening to chuck me out. Bags packed and ready in the hall. So I only went and told her, didn't I? Told her my sister had died, and I'd seen her one last time. Well, it wasn't enough and she wants to know why, why I went to see her, why it's getting to me like this, and what did happen to come between us anyway? In the end it seemed like I had no choice but to confess to her.

She chucked me out anyway so that I wished I really was having an affair – at least I'd have had some fun to show for it. So here I am, with nothing to my name but my car (I made sure I grabbed the keys) and a couple of rooms above the shop to call home.

I'm minded to go and drown my sorrows, but I know what a slippery slope that is. I've been sitting here scribbling this instead. Whoever said writing it all down helped? They haven't a bloody clue.

Undercurrents

The following day was again bathed in warm spring sunshine. Fluffy clouds chased each other across the sky in an array of animals and continents. As they walked along the lane, they compared their findings. A lamb trying to reach Australia, a cat hot on its heels.

'That vapour trail's like the fuse line to a cache of dynamite. It'll be the end of the lot, sooner or later.'

'Thanks for the cheerful contribution, Bede.' Fran shook her head at him. He remained deadpan but Elin saw the spark in his eyes.

Where the lane curved sharply towards the river, they turned off along a track into the woods. Elin loved Holtwood, the way a rise in the land created an extensive haven of trees that was different from, but in harmony with, the rest of the floodplain. She often came to sit by the riverbank here, trailing her fingers in the water the way that the trees trailed their twigs. It was all overshadowed now. For one thing, the pheasants in the new pen at the far side of the wood didn't belong there. She didn't blame the birds themselves – it was the shoot and its recent expansion that she disliked. But that was as nothing compared to Philip Northcote's other plans. The bombshell had dropped weeks, maybe months, ago when he submitted an application for a licence on his land next to Holtwood for test drilling with a view to fracking. A lively protest group had formed, centred on the community shop, and Elin sometimes felt their lives had become dominated by meetings, research, formulating and presenting arguments to the planners.

Despite her determination not to let Northcote cast a shadow over their lives – not yet, while there was still a good chance the drilling could be stopped – they'd nevertheless been coming to Holtwood less than they should since the flood two winters ago. Since Joe drowned. Single-handedly, she'd cleared the lower slopes by the riverbank of the worst of the debris, salvaging what she could. She'd even managed to coax Bede to the woods a few times to perform essential maintenance on the storm-damaged trees or to collect firewood. But it had been Joe who had initiated the long-standing agreement with Frank, the farmer who owned the woodland, to manage the trees in return for a share of the timber and the freedom to forage. The woods were one of those pockets of uncertainty where Joe's spirit still lingered, and when Fran had suggested they come here, Elin had been relieved when Bede agreed. Maybe a morning's useful activity would help drive away the ghosts.

They lost themselves in arranging logs and branches, lashing them together to form two rafts sturdy enough to get them downriver to the small gravel beach at the edge of the Alderleat land, and finding pieces to use as paddles and rudders to steer by.

After a final check of the knots, they heaved their rafts into the water. She noticed Jeff place a protective hand on Fran's arm but she shook him off. Elin forgot the moment as soon as they pushed away from the bank, letting the water take hold. The speed felt far greater than it was, the dark threat of undercurrents lurking beneath the river's innocently sluggish surface giving her a frisson of excitement. She glanced at Bede. If he was afraid, he hid it well.

Perhaps she was worrying unnecessarily. This might be the first time they'd been on the river since the flood had taken Joe, but if she thought about it, how often had they sailed on it, swam in it, before that? Maybe Bede wasn't silently struggling to overcome some inner turmoil because there was nothing left to overcome. He certainly seemed calm, studying the water in concentration. He flashed her a reassuring smile.

They drifted with the current, occasionally adjusting their line. She and Bede worked in perfect harmony, drawing steadily ahead. Elin glanced back at their two friends, then pulled deeply on her paddle as they rounded the bend towards home.

Bede straightened, flexing his shoulders and gazing downstream as the fields, house and buildings of Alderleat came into view. Beyond lay the smart gardens and roughly-mown lower field of their next-door neighbour Kate's guest house, Bankside. As they drifted in towards the bank between their flourishing willow plantation and the incongruous neatness next door, they were greeted by a ragged cheer. Elin looked up and saw a trio of men raising their glasses from around Kate's picnic table. She waved back.

'Concentrate, girl. Tricky bit coming up.'

They managed to steer themselves to within reach of the bank.

'Hold tight.' She reached out, planted her pole into the riverbed and swung them in, timber crunching against gravel.

They hauled their craft onto dry land, then laughed as Fran and Jeff missed, slurping into mud and reeds. Bede made a gentlemanly show of throwing them a rope and hauling their raft in as they picked their way onto the grass.

Elin turned to see the three guys strolling towards them. She recognised the lad Silvan, looking much the same as he had the night before, with two slightly older men in smart casual jeans and polo shirts.

'Look who it is,' she murmured to Bede. 'Doesn't look like Kate's usual kind of guest.'

Silvan grinned and waved.

'That looks fun,' one of the others called out. 'Any chance of a ride?'

'Have we got time?' The third one glanced at Silvan, who nodded.

'I'm not sure…' Bede began.

'Me and Carl have been on more activity weekends than you can count. We know what we're doing, don't you worry.'

'Guess we can't complain at you volunteering to do our work for us.'

Elin directed them over the fence and across the stream that ran from their leat down the side of the field to the river. As they approached, Silvan introduced the other two as Carl and Rob.

'So this is where you live?' he asked.

'That's right.' Elin waved her arm in the direction of the house. 'Alderleat.'

'Nice. So that turbine's yours? I've never seen one like it. You know, wooden.'

Bede smiled like a proud father. 'We wanted it to look part of the landscape. Built it with my own fair hands.' His expression suddenly clouded. 'That is, *our* fair hands. Me, Elin and…my uncle. He died not long after it was finished.'

'Sorry to hear it. It's a fitting memorial.' Silvan gazed at the serenely-turning blades for a moment then looked back at Bede. 'Well, shall we…?'

They set off up the field with the three visitors in tow, Elin smiling at her husband expounding about forestry and raft-building as though his innate practicality gave him expert status in all things. At the road they split up and the men headed for the woods while Elin and Fran went up to the house to fetch the trailer.

They were down by the river, dismantling the timber to take a second load up to the yard, when Elin heard raised voices, Jeff's rising in anger above raucous laughter. She ran down to the bank and grabbed the coil of rope in readiness. As the rafts rounded the bend Jeff was guiding one in to the bank. On his own. She caught sight of a forlorn swimmer hauling himself into the reeds higher up. The next thing she saw was a pair of logs carried by the current, followed at a distance by Carl and Rob clinging to the remnants of lashed branches.

'Get in to the side!' she yelled, grabbing the rope and readying herself to throw the loose end out to them. They caught it and began to pull themselves in, another piece of timber detaching itself from the raft as they crossed the faster flow in the middle of the river. She heard footsteps and, before she knew it, Bede was beside her, all heaving breath and cursing, hauling like a demon on the rope.

'You stupid *bastards*!'

'Hey, mate, we were just—'

'Call yourselves experienced? I was serious about the bloody dangers! This isn't a fucking playground. Not to mention the timber we've lost.' Bede gazed downstream at the fast-disappearing pieces of wood.

'These things happen,' Elin said in an attempt to pacify. 'I'm sure it wasn't their fault.'

'Bollocks! They did it deliberately. These two jokers started ramming the other two.'

'Oh, come on,' Silvan said as he walked up and reached to help Carl out of the water. The three of them stood forlornly dripping on the river bank. 'It was only—'

'I don't know what got into us,' Bede snapped. 'We should never have agreed.'

'Hey, hey.' Silvan gestured as if shushing a crowd of excitable children. 'Calm down, mate, yeah?'

'Calm down? It's such a waste! Not just our work – we sweated for hours to harvest that lot, but do you know how long it took those trees to grow? Perfectly good wood—'

Kip started barking as Bede's voice rose, and Elin caught hold of the dog's collar.

'We're sorry, right?' Silvan looked suitably apologetic, but Carl and Rob were closer to laughing.

'So, what if we'd drowned?' Rob chipped in. 'Would that make it OK? A life for a log?'

'You'd have brought it on yourselves,' Bede said.

'Oh, for God's sake, it's not the end of the world.'

Elin sighed inwardly as the embers were fanned back into flames.

'Of course it isn't! Nothing like!' Bede glared at him with the blazing intensity of an old-time preacher. 'You'll know when the end of the world hits you. And it will, sooner or later. Probably sooner, since most people carry on like you – using, consuming, chucking away without a care! You might bloody realise when it does! Might learn to show some respect.'

'A-*men*!' Carl sang out.

The tension rose a notch further.

'Look, they didn't mean any harm.' Silvan glanced at the other two. 'Got carried away. We're sorry we lost your timber, aren't we, guys?'

'Yeah, guess.'

'How about we see you down the pub later? Buy you a drink or two?'

Elin had to give Silvan credit for trying.

'I don't think so.' Bede turned abruptly to help Jeff load the wood they'd managed to salvage onto the trailer. He looked back at the three of them hovering uncertainly. 'You might as well leave us to it. Go and get dry. Haven't you got shoot business to see to?'

Silvan looked at his watch. 'Yeah, looks like it's time we weren't here. See you around.'

They walked off. Elin frowned at Bede. 'Shoot business?'

'Turns out Mr Guitar Man's really Mr Pheasant Man in disguise. New keeper drafted in by Philip to help with the expansion of the Northcote Jr empire. He's probably lining up to man Prospect G drill rigs when the time comes, too.'

She thought about the music last night and wished their second meeting with Silvan had been in better circumstances. She might even have forgiven him his job.

The sunset looked promising. After they'd cleared the dinner things and shut the chickens in to roost, they decided to spend their last evening together around the fire pit in the sheltered spot on higher ground between the house and the turbine.

'I'll bring my guitar.' Elin began to pack it into its case. 'You lot go on ahead – I'll catch you up.'

Beyond the workshop at the far end of the yard, Bede was waiting for her on the little footbridge over the leat. Elin caught him up and he grasped her in an unexpected hug.

'Thanks for waiting,' she said.

'I wanted to. I'm sorry about earlier, love. I guess I was a bit on edge before they appeared.' He glanced down at the water. 'You know… the river.'

'You don't have to explain to me. It's still not fully forgiven?'

'The river – forgiven? Don't be daft. You can't forgive a body of water for going about its natural business. *It* didn't kill Joe.'

She sighed inwardly, wondering where this was leading and how many more times he'd play it out.

'I guess we'll never know exactly what happened,' he said calmly. 'But it's like we always said – the riverflow. Things change. We move on. I should accept it was an accident.' He reached out, tilted her head and kissed her. She responded warmly. To hear him finally say those last four words was the best gift he could give her. They stood for a moment looking at the small water-wheel – still, silent and just visible in the dusk, waiting to bring the workshop to life. She loved it and all it represented: the first major change he and Joe had made to Alderleat when they moved here.

Like much of what they'd done, it hadn't gone entirely smoothly, with hostility from some outside quarters and arguments between themselves. Whether intoxicated by the anarchy of Calsthorpe Wood or antagonised by the cloud under which he'd left the community, Joe had been all for just forging ahead, saying no one could possibly accuse them of causing harm by reinstalling a water-wheel on the rusting old shaft and shoring up an existing water-course. They could always get retrospective planning permission if anyone reported them. But Bede had insisted on doing everything properly, with all the additional expense, surveys and months' delay that entailed. His obsessive nature meant he enjoyed learning and remembering the minutiae of the regulations and complying with them – in this case at least, since he agreed they made sense. He'd been vindicated in the end: because they'd followed the proper procedures to the letter, they were able to face down the few objections they'd received, and now it meant they were morally better placed to object to Philip Northcote's plans.

When they arrived at the fire pit with its wide view of Foxover, the river, the flood plain and the hills beyond, Fran and Jeff had already coaxed a small fire into life and they settled down to join them.

A few wispy clouds had gathered to adorn the sunset, swallows swooped for the evening midges and the rushing of the stream formed a constant backdrop. Fran poured out four beers and handed them round. Elin noticed Jeff's glare and Fran's answering look of defiance.

They raised their glasses to the accompaniment of the crackling fire.

'Thanks for having us,' Fran said. 'It's been lovely.'

'We're the ones thanking you,' Elin said.

Bede stopped fussing with the fire and looked up at Fran. 'Yes, I don't know where we'd be without you.'

'Oh, we love what you're doing here. It's good to feel part of it.' Fran smiled at him. It was obvious that she knew what he meant. Not this time particularly, but her extended stays had kept Elin going during the last eighteen months. She raised her glass to her lips. 'Your beer's as amazing as ever, Elin. Doing that brew together the other day really took me back to the old uni days.'

'You remember the looks we used to get taking home-brewed ale to parties?' Elin was relieved at the change of subject. 'All those comments about being cheapskate.'

Fran grinned. 'Everyone complaining at us taking over the kitchen, moaning about the smell? They were more appreciative at Calsthorpe, of course. *They* knew all about the important things in life.'

Bede frowned at her reference to the protest camp; to Elin's relief, Fran didn't seem to notice.

'I'm definitely going to get back into it once we're home. Hey, Jeff?'

He held up his glass and critically examined the amber contents.

'Well, *I'd* enjoy it,' he said. 'Aren't you supposed to be—?'

Fran's slight shake of the head silenced him.

'What's this about?' Elin said.

Fran picked up a stick, leaned towards the bonfire and nudged a branch into position, releasing a display of sparks. She sat back with a barely perceptible sigh. 'Oh, it's early days and we weren't going to tell anyone yet, but…' She reached out and took Jeff's hand.

A swallow swooped so close Elin heard its wings thrum. Jeff glanced at Bede who was fastening and unfastening the top button of his shirt, gazing into the fire.

'We're expecting,' Fran announced.

Bede looked round. Elin was surprised to see his expression light up.

'That's brilliant news.' He hugged Fran, shook Jeff's hand. 'Congratulations!'

Elin felt a flood of warmth as she embraced her friend. So that explained the non-drinking, and Jeff's fussing over Fran by the river. She sat back, looking fondly at Bede and wondering whether he'd go all protective around her if she were pregnant. She swallowed hard. Told herself firmly to get a grip, that it wasn't going to happen.

'Thanks,' Fran said to him. 'I know what you think, but—'

'Oh, don't mind what I think. Your choice.' Bede stared

into the flames then looked up as if gaining strength from them. 'I think you'll make a wonderful family. And mind you don't skimp on the visits to Uncle Bede and Aunty Elin.'

'Quite an education.' Jeff grinned. 'Who needs school?'

'They'll need more than school to equip them for the way the world's going.'

'Bede…' Elin put a hand on his arm.

'Sorry.' He hunched forward, hugging his knees. The air beyond the fireglow seemed momentarily colder.

'I knew we shouldn't have said anything,' Jeff said. 'I thought you being pleased for us was too good to be true.'

'I wasn't the one brought up "what I think". I meant it when I said I'm delighted for you. Of course I am.' He reached out to stroke Kip, and smiled apologetically at Elin. 'Let's have some music to celebrate.'

She unpacked the guitar and began to play her favourite riversong, the threat of an atmosphere carried away with the soothing chords and the woodsmoke as they sang and talked. After a while Kip stirred, sat up and looked expectantly at Bede.

'Looks like it's time for a walk,' he announced, getting to his feet. 'Nothing personal, but…you know…'

'Since when did you need our permission?' Jeff said. Fran glared at him.

'Quite.' Bede squeezed Elin's shoulder. 'See you later.'

He strode off over the rise into the night. Suddenly gone.

'Do you want to go after him?' Fran asked Elin.

'He'll be fine. Always comes back as if nothing's happened.'

'I didn't know anything had,' Jeff said.

Elin and Fran exchanged a look.

The footpath snaked ahead, barely visible in the darkness. Kip sniffed inquisitive rings around Bede, and the wind ruffled his hair. Any awkwardness he felt about leaving, about all that lay beneath the conversation they'd just had, was soon dispelled by the guilty pleasure of being on his own for a while.

As he reached higher ground, the view opened up. Quiet grey fields stretched beyond the nearby lights of Foxover, with scattered villages hugging the distant hillsides on the far side of the floodplain. He tried to ignore the orange haze on the skyline, reflecting up to the low cloud. All those resources used for little more than light pollution. He wondered briefly about reviving their unpopular campaign to have the village street lights turned off at midnight. So much had been smothered by other concerns recently.

As a small boy he'd spent hours at bedtime gazing out of his window at a very different view of densely packed lines of orange lights winding across the hillside opposite. If he narrowed his eyes, the street lights became points of fire, merging to one huge conflagration. Whole streets, the whole district, in flames. He always wondered whether this was the one; maybe this time there was a fire and no one had noticed. He'd send himself to sleep devising strategies to escape from his room should the blaze spread to their street. After his mum married and his stepbrothers came along, he'd made the mistake of telling them. Their ridicule had driven any thoughts of rescue from his escape plans.

Kip came rustling from the undergrowth and he reached down to feel the familiar fur beneath his hand. The clouds shifted constantly, occasional glimpses of moonlight highlighting the contours of the land.

He still sometimes saw the orange glow pooling out of an underbelly of cloud as a warning of some apocalyptic disaster. But it wouldn't begin with vast orange glows on the horizon. People were that little bit too clever, if not clever enough. They'd always stem the immediate tide without seeing the bigger picture. Each attempt to staunch the haemorrhage was only delaying it, burying it, sweeping it from view. Things would start to fail, like a system's components, to be replaced individually at first until it became so much that a new system was needed. But you couldn't build a new Earth.

Despite his anger and helplessness, he derived a perverse comfort from the inevitability that the Earth would continue in some form regardless of what mankind threw at her, and unless people changed their ways – and soon – would become hostile to humans in the same way as a body rid itself of disease. It was all so much bigger than him; his immediate problems hardly seemed to matter in the face of such huge forces.

He called Kip and walked on.

'I'm sorry about the timing.' Fran leaned forward and raked the dying embers. 'I know kids are a touchy subject between you two.'

Elin sighed, gazing across the fire towards the path down which Jeff had vanished, yawning, a few moments ago. 'All the more reason to share your excitement.'

'But is that why…?' Fran waved up the rise.

'I doubt it. He was feeling stressed after this afternoon's encounter.'

She looked away from the fire and watched the stars

become ever more dense between the ribbons of cloud as her eyes readjusted to the dark.

'I hope we haven't overstayed our welcome.'

'Now you really are talking daft.'

'You'd said things were finally settling down between you, and it was certainly looking that way. Now he's gone stomping off.'

Elin shrugged. She understood the need to be alone.

'You've got the patience of a saint.'

Fran seemed to think of their marriage as a perpetual struggle; she'd advised Elin against getting involved with Bede right from the start. But as the years went by and he gained confidence, Fran had begun to admit she'd been wrong: Bede hadn't been aloof or boorish, but merely shy. Yet although she'd come to appreciate his and Elin's love for one another, it didn't stop her referring to him as a moody and difficult man who needed dealing with. Elin and Bede, on the other hand, considered themselves a perfect team – her creativity and home-making provided the heart, while his technical know-how made it possible. It was a crude generalisation; they were each capable of both passion and practicality. But neither would function so well without the other. As proved by nearly fifteen years of marriage. Of course, Elin knew that Fran, her own family and others were only supporting her, seeing things from what they believed to be her perspective. Who did Bede have to take his side, to confide in occasionally? Joe, and Joe was gone. No wonder the last year and a half had been so difficult for them both. She understood, but was relieved that his time for grieving seemed to have passed.

7th April 1999

Today I finally got my chance to give Robert Markham a piece of my mind.

I found out recently that our Bede's been getting bullied, mainly by his step-brother, the older one, Gavin. He only told me because last time we met, he'd obviously been scrapping and I asked him what happened. He just shrugged it off like it was a fact of life (it is, it seems), or like he's bloody Jesus or something. He told me he can look after himself and not to worry. But I do. That bloody coward's three years older than him for a start – should pick on someone his own size. I've been dying to go round and teach the bastard a lesson – both of them, seeing as the younger one doesn't sound much better. If not them, the stepfather, who it seems is only too happy to turn a blind eye.

But I dare say our Bede would be mortified. (Funny the way I can't help calling him 'our Bede'.) Seems it's not usually physical, more a case of nicking pocket money, pranks, destroying homework, endless drip drip drip. Of course he doesn't help by insisting on long hair, the way he dresses, pushing the bounds of what's allowed by school uniform.

I tried to find a way to tread carefully and asked why didn't he just get his hair cut for an easier life? And he tells me to shut up, his mum never used to nag him about it. He suddenly gives me this look, confiding like, and said he wondered if maybe she'd let him get away with it because his dad had hair like that and it was some kind of remembrance? I was floored, first time he'd asked me about his dad, and I struggled for a moment to remember what the guy looked like. Where on earth did he come up with a notion like that?

Well, to Robert Markham.

It was a presentation evening at our Bede's school, for the Design & Tech pupils who'd entered some local industry-sponsored invention competition. He'd put together a solar-powered electric bike contraption – panels all over the panniers, a complicated gizmo to switch in when an energy boost's needed. More clever than effective and hardly practical or stylish – let's just say I doubt he's going to become one of these teenage millionaires on the back of it. But what do I know? I was well impressed by his research and ability to put it all into practice.

Anyway, I walked in and saw him standing behind his table, looking generally chuffed but with a big dose of his characteristic awkwardness, and a woman with a name badge who looked like his teacher was there chatting away to a fella about my age, one of the judges I assumed.

Bede mumbles an introduction – his teacher, Mrs Harris I think it was. I shook her hand and said something about how proud I was of our Bede and he told her I've been such a help to him. At this the other fella turns his plastic smile to me and tells me he's Robert Markham, Bede's dad.

'Good to meet you at last,' he says. At last!! As if I should've asked his permission to get involved in my nephew's life! Bede's out of Markham's line of sight and he mouths STEPdad at me, but I ignored him and quickly said something like, you must be proud too, and shook his hand. As Markham blathered something about giving him every encouragement with this project, I remembered what our Bede had told me about Gavin breaking some intricate component that took ages to repair, and then 'losing' the folder all his early designs were in so he was up all night writing the portfolio out again to hand it in. His stepdad hadn't believed him, of course. Not even when Bede found the original folder – badly disguised, contents gone forever – in Gavin and Sam's room. He just got told off for snooping through his brothers' things.

We enjoyed the prizegiving. Our Bede won the under 16s, so he got tied up talking to the local paper, and there was my chance. Over a coffee that tasted like cat's pee, I got Robert Markham on his own and asked straight out if he was aware of all the grief his sons, Gavin in particular, were causing Bede. He just looks at me with this disbelieving face on and says, 'I might have known.'

I said he could hardly blame the lad for telling me.

'Telling you what?' His voice was raised, making me glance round. 'How much I've gone out my way to treat him as my own son? Kids, boys in particular, are always arguing and I've taken Bede's side more than I should. But he rejected us from the start.' I think I was shaking my head in disbelief. 'And he's getting worse,' the hard-nosed bastard goes on.

'Give him a break. Lad's not long since lost his mother.'

'My boys lost their mother, too, but when I married Lydia they didn't go round looking for someone to blame. They came to love her as much as their own mum, and they'd have loved Bede as a brother if he'd have let them. He's made a career of tale-telling, setting things up, lying to get them into trouble.'

I made it clear that's not what I'd heard.

'You've got his word for it,' he says. 'I'm giving you mine.'

He suddenly shut up. I glanced to the side and saw our

Bede standing there. For how long? I made some comment about the newspaper interview and rambled on about getting a copy. He nodded to me, then turned to Markham.

'Trying to take Joe away from me too, are you?'

'Don't be daft.' Markham does a kind of half-laugh like it's all a big mountain out of a molehill. He points at me and gives it, 'He was the one started shit-stirring.'

Whatever the rights and wrongs, did he look the tiniest bit embarrassed? Did he make any attempt to explain to the lad, or reassure him, claim that he'd misheard?

No. 'He started it.' For fuck's sake.

Markham turned to me, still with that jovial just-family-banter-we-don't-really-mean-it air. 'I don't know about Design & Tech, he should be up for the drama prize.' He gives this award-winning melodramatic shrug of his own. 'Know what I mean?'

Our Bede's sleeping at my flat, on the sofa, for tonight. To be honest, it feels good to have someone else in the bloody soulless place.

Innocents

Leaving the men to load the bags and a box or two of fresh produce into the car, Elin turned to Fran.

'You won't be travelling this light for a while once Junior arrives.'

Fran smiled. 'A price worth paying. But yeah, I've got plans to make the most of my freedom while it lasts.'

'Going anywhere nice?'

'Nothing that compares to here. Actually, I'm planning on spending more time with the protesters at the fracking site. You know, now they're starting test drilling in Lancashire.' She put a protective hand on her midriff and glanced over towards Jeff. 'I guess it'll mainly be monitoring and observing duties – I'm under strict instructions not to do anything physical or get arrested.' She grinned conspiratorially. 'We'll see about that.'

Elin thought of Holtwood with a heavy heart. 'I can't believe it's actually happening. How can they be so stupid?'

Fran waved vaguely upriver. 'I really hope you manage to nip this one in the bud. In the meantime, why don't you get some practice in? Come and join us. Different place, same fossil fuels.'

Needled by guilt, Elin focused past her friend on the greenhouse. 'I'll see how things go. Busy time of year. Hopefully we can—'

'Come on, Elin, it's a decade and a half since Calsthorpe! There's always an excuse. You haven't done anything except a couple of demos since you two got married and holed up here.'

'Haven't done anything? Holed up? What do you think *this* is all about?'

Fran nudged her playfully. 'Only kidding. I know – living it rather than shouting about it. But there comes a time when you have to shout.'

'You think I don't know that? We're doing a decent job of getting the village mobilised, aren't we?'

Her eyebrows raised, Fran looked over to where Bede and Jeff were peering beneath the raised bonnet of the car. 'I must admit he's improved, but he's still making you a bit thin-skinned. You know I think the world of Alderleat. Just a bit of friendly banter. I mean it, though, Elin. I'd love it if you joined us for a few days, even if it's just to back me up when I remind Jeff that pregnancy isn't an illness, that a new life means we have to fight all the more for the future.' As if he'd heard his name, Jeff lowered the bonnet and beckoned them over. 'Uh-oh. Looks like it's time to go.'

Elin felt the lingering warmth of friendship as they stood in the gateway and watched the car disappear down the lane. The wind whipped clouds across the sky, trailed along the ground to ruffle grass and tickle willow leaves, and stirred up glistening wavelets on the surface of the river beyond. She waved, even though there was only Bede left to see her.

'What was that about being in touch?' he asked. 'What are you two plotting?'

'Plotting! Nothing sinister – joining forces between Frack-Free Foxover and the campaigns she's involved with up north. Don't look at me like that. Honestly, Bede – this is real. We've got to stop it, or at least do everything we can to try. And, you know, we might need their help one day. This isn't going to go away by wishing.'

'So we'll pitch in if we're needed,' he said. 'Yeah, 'course we will.'

Don't sound so enthusiastic, she thought, putting the subject aside to work on again later. 'So, are you going to help me plant out those seedlings?'

'There's plenty I want to see to in the workshop, but if you need me—'

'I do. Though I guess we can allow ourselves a cuppa first.'

After putting the kettle on, Bede moved his phone back to its usual charging spot on the windowsill by the kitchen table, which had been taken over by Jeff's tablet for the duration of their stay. Elin fondly imagined his relief. He'd barely concealed his irritation at the request for a socket where the wifi was strongest, not only because it meant Jeff would spend ages absorbed in some virtual world or obsessing about work e-mails, but because it disrupted Bede's desire to have everything in its proper place. He'd even complained the other day about the key to the workshop being on the wrong hook.

She looked from the flowers on the table by the window – for once put there by Bede, in honour of her birthday – to her cards arranged on the dresser. She'd have to get a frame for the wonderful painting by one of the old Calsthorpe crowd that Fran had tracked down. There was a *Pen-blwydd Hapus* from her mum and dad and a jokey one from her sister Carys and husband Andy in Canada, brimming inside with kisses from her little nephew and niece. Elin wondered when she'd see them again. Coming with Bede to Alderleat when they married meant she hadn't achieved her ambition of returning to live in Wales, though they were only a few miles short of the border and at least she was a lot closer than her sister was. Despite the distances separating the small Jones clan, she was glad of her family's normality compared to Bede's.

He turned as he waited for the rumbling kettle to come to the boil. 'Penny for them.'

She smiled. 'Just admiring my cards and flowers.'

The kettle rattled to its climax and he poured, then came to the table with the teapot and mugs.

'What about their news, then?' he said as he sat down. 'Fran expecting. Who'd have thought it?'

She fought a sudden lump in her throat. She'd woken in the night and lain there unable to sleep. Despite her protestations to Fran, the effect of their friends' news combined with the intangible ticking clock of her birthday had surprised her with its intensity.

'Great, isn't it?' she managed.

He beamed at her. Not the reaction she'd expected. She felt a small bubble of hope.

'Imagine us,' he said, 'aunty and uncle with our own ready-made borrowed sprog whenever they need a bit of breathing space. As he-or-she grows we can teach him-or-her what a proper way of life is and get some help around the place into the bargain.'

'It'll be lovely,' she said. 'But…' she ignored his warning look, 'doesn't it make you want more than borrowed?'

With an almost imperceptible shake of his head, he turned to the window. Knowing her bubble was about to burst, Elin waited for his response: you knew how I felt when we got married. I haven't changed.

'I wish I felt differently,' he said eventually. 'I hate to think I'm making you unhappy. But I can't imagine…'

They'd been through it all before. The way the overpopulated world was going, he couldn't face bringing an innocent child into it, any more than he could bring himself to exacerbate the problem by adding to the numbers. She'd shared his point of view until recently, but was beginning to find that emotion, instinct and biology were stronger than intellect or ideology, and that she hated hearing him talk like this.

'It's as if you've abandoned all hope for the future.' He remained silent as she fought down the threat of tears. 'Do you really think the world's population crisis, or even the country's, is going to be solved by Elin and Bede Sherwell remaining childless?'

'I'm not daft. But…'

'But it's a matter of principle.' She picked up the teapot and poured. As she passed his mug to him she put it down a little too hard, causing hot tea to splash over and pool around the base. 'Can't you imagine passing your bloody principles on to a future generation? Who do you think's going to save the world after you?'

'I've no pretensions about saving the world,' he muttered. 'Anyway, I thought they were *our* principles, *our* vision.'

He took a towel from the back of his chair and wiped the spillage.

'Yes. Ours,' she conceded. 'But, you know, the world needs people who think, who care, who are prepared to do things differently.'

Bede took a sip of his tea and put the mug down, adjusting it to sit precisely between two knots in the wood of the tabletop. Elin felt like shoving it out of line.

'All this talk of population,' she said. 'It's just an excuse. You can't hack the idea of responsibility.'

'Thanks, Elin. Thanks a bunch.'

His head was bowed, hair hiding his face. She'd succeeded in hurting him – petty vengeance – and almost regretted it.

'Bede…'

He jerked his head up and looked straight at her. 'OK,

yes, I do find that kind of responsibility hard to face. You know why.' She did. She wished he'd get over it, then hated herself for the thought. 'I just can't see myself as a dad, all right? Surely it's better to admit it now than make some irreversible mistake. Can't you respect that?'

'Can't *you* put the past behind you and respect what *I* want—' She just managed to stop herself adding *for once*. 'What's so bloody awful about it anyway? You've always enjoyed having Carys's kids here. You love showing them things, teaching them stuff.'

He gave her a grudging nod. 'Can't we see how we get on with Fran and Jeff's first? They're like extended family. Look how it was with me and Joe. Special relationships can mean just as much.'

She sighed, reached out and took his hand. 'I'm not talking about a relationship, however special, with *a* child. I'm talking about *our* child. A part of me and you. Don't you get that?'

'Sorry, love, I wish…' He squeezed her hand gently. 'Believe me, I know what it means to you.'

'The clock's ticking, Bede. Can't hold it back.'

'And I can't just turn around and change who I am and how I feel, all right?'

He gulped his tea down. She took the mug from him, pushed her chair out noisily and went over to the sink. Her eyes were welling and she didn't want him to see.

'Didn't you have something in the workshop to see to?' she said quietly.

'I thought we were talking—'

'There's no point playing it over and over like a stuck record, is there?'

He came up behind her, put a hand on her shoulder. 'You OK, love?'

'Of course.' She brushed a hand over her eyes, turned and forced a smile. 'Go and do your stuff. I'll be out in the greenhouse.'

She stood for a moment looking at the back door he'd closed behind him, her regret at the inevitable outcome tinged with near gratitude that they were once again able to have that kind of conversation at all.

Bede straightened and looked with satisfaction at the steady green light. He'd found the short-circuit, and the batteries should be back to taking the charge from the turbine. It had only taken a little patience. Like Elin's seemingly endless patience with him. After half an hour of absorbed concentration he felt calmer, but wished there was a solution to her growing desire for a family and his terror of the idea.

Wait around long enough and the decision will have made itself for you. Is that what you want?

Of course not. He closed his eyes momentarily; tried to blink away the voice, if not the point of the words. He was being irrational, he knew, with his persistence in his resentment of the faceless, nameless bastard who had abandoned his pregnant mother, and his failure to truly put the Markhams behind him. But he was still convinced that humans' inability to live sustainably on the planet was due largely to overpopulation. That wasn't irrational. Of course, Elin could be right that he didn't have any hope for the future. Whether or not he could answer that one, he knew how much a child meant to her. Maybe he could consider it. *Maybe*. The word induced such a tangible fear that he realised he was shaking his head in denial.

He busied himself with putting his tools away neatly, then walked over to the door. The regular popping of the clay-pigeon shoot somewhere in the distance insisted its way towards him on the breeze: a distasteful reminder of the real shoot that would replace the clays when the season came around. The sound of the guns irritated him, rekindling his anger at yesterday's riverside face-off.

Bede went back into the workshop and took the axe from among the tools lining the wall. Reassuring himself with a brief glance at the green light of the inverter, he went out to the timber stack behind the workshop and began to chop firewood. As he lost himself in the rhythm, he allowed himself a moment of pride in what they'd achieved. Proving it was possible to live sustainably without compromising on comfort, harnessing technology and using his fascination for all things mechanical to serve a worthwhile purpose. Yes, he allowed himself pride, satisfaction, though he recognised they weren't going to change the world. Even Elin sometimes conceded that they were not so much teaching by example as simply living by their consciences. Despite his reputation for mouthing off, he found it hard to see himself as an ambassador for a cause, and on top of that, he was even beginning to doubt the direction in which they were heading.

They'd tried to spread the word with Sunny Days. Based on Bede's practical skills, Elin's head for organisation and their old friend Steve Day's combination of an electrician's qualifications with golden-tongued salesmanship, they had established a small business installing solar panels and the occasional mini-turbine in homes around the region. But in the turmoil following Joe's death, Bede's contribution had grown erratic, and as his belief in what they were doing became more shaky – trying to stem the tide by replacing resource-hungry consumption with slightly more sustainable consumption – Steve's tolerance had been tried to the limits and he'd eventually gone his own way. It had been several months since they'd heard from him. Bede and Elin still needed to make a living and drumming up custom for himself was not his forte. He really had let things go. Maybe it was time to give Steve a call.

He stopped to gather the split logs into a wheelbarrow and take them over to stack in the shelter. The burble of Elin's radio drifted across to him from the greenhouse, interspersed with the sporadic shots, as their cockerel crowed an intermittant elegy for the hapless pheasants being reared for probable death in a few months' time.

He heard another splutter of distant guns from the shoot. What a way to spend a weekend. Not to mention all the months spent breeding excess numbers of birds that didn't belong there, for the sole purpose of being blasted from the sky for entertainment. Local employment? Surely they could find something more useful to do. As he turned to gather another load of logs, he caught a glint of sunlight off a car approaching along the winding lane from the village.

Kip began to bark as the car turned into their yard. Bede straightened, silenced the dog with a stern word and strolled over, running his fingers through his hair in an attempt to look presentable.

Elin had approached the man from the car; he towered over her but that did nothing to diminish her attitude of defiance. Bede recognised the young local policeman from Halbury. They'd never really met, although he'd said hello to him in the bar of the Horseshoes a few times.

'Bede Sherwell, isn't it?'

'That's me.' He offered his hand, which Will Elsworth shook as he introduced himself. 'What can I do for you?'

'There's was a bit of an incident last night at the breeding pen in Holtwood. You know where I mean?'

'Sure.' The breeding pen that didn't belong in Holtwood. 'What kind of incident?'

'A whole load of young pheasants let loose, the enclosure smashed and left wide open. A fox clearly finished what the vandals started. Carnage. And to top it all, "Murderers" daubed in red paint across the gate.'

'Sorry to hear it.' Bede shook his head in sympathy. 'So how can we help?'

'Where were you last night?'

'You what? Hold on a minute. Just because—'

'We need to check, that's all.'

Noting Elin's warning look, Bede took a deep breath and calmly told Will about their evening routine followed by the bonfire in the far field.

'And you went straight back to the house after that?'

He glanced at Elin. 'I went for a walk.'

Will's eyebrows shot up. 'What time?'

Bede shrugged. 'Half past ten?'

Elin confirmed it and moved close to him.

'What time did you get home?'

'About an hour later,' Elin said firmly. 'There's nothing unusual about Bede going off for a walk. He likes to be on his own sometimes, you know? And he set off in completely the wrong direction for Holtwood, *if* that's what you're implying.'

'You've been warned about vandalism in that area before.'

'A few anti-fracking posters?' Bede tried to keep his voice calm. 'There's a bit of a difference.'

'Also, Mrs Henderson's guests were admiring the moonlight when they saw someone – tall, long-haired – walk up the footpath over there. They arrived for the clay shoot first thing this morning and heard about the incident from Philip Northcote's keepers. Apparently you had a run-in with them yesterday?'

'You've got to be joking! It was only a bit of verbal. Nothing to do with the shoot.'

'"A bit of verbal". What happened?'

He and Elin described the events as best they could.

'I'm told your behaviour was threatening. Carl Smith says you "went mental". You were about to set your dog on him and your wife had to hold you back.'

'Oh, please. Carl Smith is exaggerating,' Elin said firmly. 'Anyway, what's that got to do with liberating pheasants?'

'"Liberating." Do you sympathise with the vandals?'

'Just a turn of phrase,' she said. 'It's used a lot.'

'In some circles, perhaps.' He raised his eyebrows before turning back to Bede. 'I've got to ask – what shoes were you wearing?'

With a haze of anger building inside him, Bede glanced down at his work boots. 'My sandals, wasn't it, El?'

'Please can I see them?' Will looked pointedly at the shoe rack that was visible just inside the cottage door.

Trying to stay calm, Bede fetched the sandals, and a pair of wellingtons for good measure. Will checked them against a photo of a sole print, then narrowed his eyes as he passed them back.

'Looks like you're in the clear,' he said, stowing the photo away and moving towards the car.

'You might as well check these while you're at it.' Bede thrust his hands out. 'No red paint beneath the fingernails. You're welcome to search the sheds for cans, wet paintbrushes. Honestly, it's not my style – but if a man's "gone mental" you never know what he might do without realising.'

Will fixed him with a stare. 'I'm sorry to have disturbed you. But if you hear anything, do let us know.'

Bede stood, hands shoved into his pockets, as he and Elin watched the car disappear down the lane. She touched his arm and the tension ebbed a little. As the engine noise faded into the summer air, they heard another faint volley of distant guns.

'Did you have to be so antagonistic?' she asked.

'He provoked me.' Bede turned to her, unease seeping through him. 'I suppose you're going to ask me what really happened.'

She rose to the bait. 'So? What did?'

He stared out over the yard and beyond, hens pecking unconcerned, produce calmly growing in the garden, the willows a rustling audience to the river minding its own leisurely business as it slid past. He couldn't believe she felt the need to question him. 'I went for a walk, didn't I?'

He started to trudge back to the woodpile.

'Bede, wait.' He paused and turned. She flashed him her smile, the one that always won him round. 'Of course I know you'd never go off and have all the fun without me.'

'Liberating captive birds, you mean?' He couldn't help grinning. 'Did you say you wanted a hand in there?'

'Thought you'd never ask.'

He would have preferred to go back to the logs but, relieved that he seemed to have been forgiven after their earlier disagreement, he wanted to be with her.

'I can't believe they'd do that,' he said as he ducked slightly beneath the greenhouse door. 'Those guys from yesterday. Naming me for no good reason.'

'You didn't exactly show them your best side.'

'They didn't show me theirs, and I didn't go blaming them for some fictitious crime.'

Elin pointed him in the direction of a tray of seedlings. 'Philip Northcote probably put them up to accusing you. You know what he's like. Pompous git.'

'Huh. If ever *I* have a go at him, you start on about slander.'

'Maybe because you're implying murder.'

He shook his head. 'Slander means lies. I'm only pointing out facts. He started sniffing round here a couple of years ago, buying back additional land – we know what for now, don't we? – and planning to do up the Grange. Lo and behold, shortly after he arrived—'

'You can't blame him for the flood.'

'But—'

'Don't.'

He turned to the tray of young plants and concentrated hard on transplanting them to the soil Elin had prepared, trying in vain not to give in to the thoughts that nagged like an addiction.

'I still think Joe could have known something—'

'Bede.'

'—before Philip was ready to unleash his plans on the village.' The planting abandoned, his hands were working uselessly, rubbing compost between his fingers as if to break each grain into its constituent atoms. 'But it's like today, isn't it? Whoever it was that reported this, you'd think the police would have better things to do. But Northcote points the finger, they follow. Just as he pointed it away from Joe drowning and they stopped trying.'

'You see?' Elin said, her tone of voice resigned to going through the motions. 'Slander.'

'Surely I can talk freely to you? What about the blow to his head? Fact. The movement I saw in the willows? Fact.'

'Debris in the river. Wind and rain.'

He continued undeterred down the path of obsession. 'Northcote was back in Foxover after years of absence. He and Joe had history. Now his fracking plans have come to light, it seems hc had a motive.'

'He also had an alibi. Honestly, Bede, what makes you think Joe knew a thing? That very "history" means they were hardly likely to sit down and have a cosy chat about it, were they? Please.' Elin closed her eyes and opened them again as if blinking some inner strength to the surface. 'You said you were going to let it go. You've said it before. I don't know why I keep believing you.'

There was a catch in her voice that got to him. She was right – no point dragging it all up again like a corpse from the mud.

'I want to let it go,' he said. 'I'm doing my best to mean it, love.'

He went over and put his arms round her from behind.

'I know.' She reached back and touched his cheek briefly before pushing him away. 'You're getting my T-shirt mucky.'

Beneath the reassurance of her teasing, he sensed her lingering unease.

What goes on

Bede hunched into his waterproof cape and cycled down the lane. His resolve to try and embrace all weathers was pushed to its limits as he turned to wave to Elin and was rewarded by a cold trickle of rainwater down his neck. Weaving his way among the large puddles that had gathered on the tarmac surface, he wondered whether he'd manage to look presentable for his first night at the Horseshoes.

He'd been as amazed as anyone at Brian's proposal that he or Elin help out behind the bar on busy nights. Elin had said she had enough on with managing the Storehouse and her part-time research at the nature reserve, and since his own work with Sunny Days was non-existent at the moment, it fell to him.

The rain was taking a breather as he reached the bridge. He was early and feeling irrationally nervous, so he stopped, pushed his hood back and leaned his bike against the ancient stone parapet. Resting his elbows on the low wall, he looked down into the rushing flow, aware from the corner of his eye of the damp, folded umbrellas in the waterside beer-garden like forlorn statues of Sabrina, the goddess of the river. Now the moment had arrived, he feared the prospect of maintaining a public veneer of affability while some of the regulars baited him – intentionally or accidentally; it made no difference – and took offence if he spoke his mind.

Why keep thinking the worst?

Bede took a sharp breath and looked around. He used to

find it comforting, but was beginning to wish the voice would leave him alone. He nevertheless allowed his negativity to dissolve into the swirling water below him and wash away. Why shouldn't he enjoy this? He was efficient and honest and could raise a smile at most of the right moments. Brian and Angela had warmed to him since he'd helped out during the floods. As he emerged from the black months that had followed Joe's death, the pub had been a refuge whenever he, and Elin in particular, needed to get out from Alderleat. The lingering contempt among a few people had turned to friendly ribbing as new-found friendships dusted his uncle's shadow from him. Even so, he'd never have imagined it extending to bar work, and briefly wondered if the suggestion had been a ploy of Elin's to keep him outward-looking and sociable. But her surprise had seemed genuine.

As he wheeled his bike round to the wooden shelter at the back of the Horseshoes, he saw Brian coming out of a store with a crate of mixers.

'Hiya, Eco.' The landlord put the crate down and watched Bede lock his bike up. 'Good and early. Plenty of time to show you the ropes before the rush. Oh, and before I forget, any chance you could have a look at the car in the next couple of days? It's cutting out, one of those annoying intermittent faults, you know?'

'Sure. I'll give it the once-over.'

Despite his hard-learned expertise, Bede had as little as possible to do with internal combustion engines these days, and Sunny Days had allowed him to leave the repair garage in Halbury where he'd worked when they first moved to Alderleat. But Brian's was one he deigned to repair and service, especially since he ran it on the biodiesel the Sherwells made from waste oil, much of it from the pub kitchens – and since, to be honest, they needed the money.

Bede picked up the crate of bottles. 'Let me help you with those.'

Brian indicated where to take them, then showed him the routines behind the bar. The easy part. He had no concerns about knowing where things went, working the till, the mental arithmetic of taking orders. It was the social side that felt daunting. He reminded himself of some of the curmudgeons he'd seen behind bars in his time and thought he could do better than that, at least.

'I'll leave you to it, then,' Brian said before disappearing to join Angie in the kitchen. 'Maisie'll be here any minute. In the meantime you know where we are if you need anything.' He moved to go, paused. 'And remember – no preaching.'

Bede waved him away cheerfully. A couple of people had come to the bar and expressed surprise at seeing him there. As he served them, he listened to their chatter about the week of early summer weather they'd had and how they were now back to wind and rain if they were lucky, gloomy drizzle the rest of the time, and where had the proper seasons gone? Remembering Brian's playful warning, he suppressed the obvious comment about humans' irreparable devastation of the climate.

The usual Friday evening regulars were trickling in, giving him a chance to get used to things before it got busy later on. Maisie, an old hand behind the bar, seemed a little wary of him at first, but her coolness gradually faded as they worked together and both began to relax. He felt as though he could even begin to enjoy it.

He was stacking the glass washer, making a mental note to talk to Brian about eco-friendly detergent, when Silvan appeared. Maisie had gone to take a food order to the kitchen and Bede was on his own.

'Evening,' he said neutrally.

Silvan returned the greeting and ordered a bottle of exotic continental lager. Bede silently questioned the taste of someonc who preferred that to the local ale in the pumps, not to mention the carbon footprint of an imported bottle – the final nail in the coffin of his initial impression that here was an interesting guy to get to know.

'Sorry about last week,' Silvan said as Bede poured the bottle into the appropriate glass. 'That business with the logs.'

Bede passed his drink over the bar. 'Forget it. I have.'

'Seriously, mate,' Silvan said. 'I'm sure those guys didn't mean to—'

'I said forget it.' He turned to put the bottle in the empties crate.

'Can I get you a drink?'

'Thanks, but some other time. No alcohol on duty.'

Silvan raised his glass and glanced at the door as if waiting for someone. Bede willed them to arrive. He picked up a cloth and began to give the bar an unnecessary wipe.

'I guess you don't approve of why I'm here.'

Bede paused. 'Who am I to approve or disapprove? I was surprised when I found out, that's all.'

He attempted a smile as he straightened the bar towels.

'It's not exactly a vocation.' Silvan leaned forward conspiratorially. 'I feel you're the sort of person I can tell. I've been living in Birmingham these last few years, but my girlfriend, who'd stayed in Oswestry, heard about Philip Northcote's job and persuaded me to go for it, come back homeward so we could be a bit closer together. Though it was just my luck that she finished with me almost as soon as I'd arrived. I have to say I'm missing the city, though I still go back for band rehearsals and gigs.

Anyway, I'm enjoying the change of scene for now – seeing a bit of country life, finding out what goes on. You get me?'

He sounded as though he were implying something. Bede had no desire to get involved with him, though Elin might say his inside knowledge could be useful to the Frack-Free Foxover group and would probably chide him for a wasted opportunity.

'Do you like what you've seen so far?'

'Actually, I do. I didn't expect an opportunity for music, for a start. Or to come across people on my wavelength, like you and Elin.'

Bede frowned: on his wavelength? 'I was thinking more about your work.'

'Oh, it seems fine. The birds, the dogs, the land – all well cared for.' He smiled. 'The keepers' accommodation isn't too bad, either. Though I'm not sure about the clients. Don't know what it'll be like when the season starts and the real hoorays arrive. They'll probably treat us like dirt.'

Bede gave a brief nod of sympathy, but what did the guy expect? There was something else on his mind and he decided to get in first. 'What did you think about the incident last week?'

'The vandalism? Don't ask me. Do you think it was something to do with your anti-fracking lot? Though I can't see the relevance.' He studied Bede, who kept his expression neutral. 'I've heard there are a few people round here who've got it in for Philip.'

'People like Elin and me?'

Silvan's expression was one of wide-eyed innocence. 'Look, I'm an honest guy. I won't pretend it didn't cross my mind you might know something. So, spill the beans – you can trust me not to say anything.'

Bede shook his head. 'First I heard of it was from the policeman who came to interrogate me.'

'Shit, you had the pigs on your case?' He frowned. 'How come?'

'No idea. Listen, Elin and I think it was as stupid as anyone would. Whatever we think about the shoot, there's no point meeting senseless waste with senseless waste, is there?' That raised a smile from Silvan. 'Those rearing pens are on the edge of a patch of woodland we help to manage, as it happens. And we don't want to risk losing it – and with it the opportunity to keep tabs on Northcote's potential fracking site.'

'Fair enough.' Silvan looked round as a couple of lads Bede recognised as gamekeepers walked in. Silvan bought them a round and they all went to sit by the fireplace. They were followed soon after by Philip Northcote, who waved over at the keepers' table as he approached the bar, his expression darkening when he saw who was behind it. Bede glanced at Maisie and excused himself with an unnecessary visit to the cellar. Better to avoid a scene on his first night. When he got back, he saw Northcote was still by the bar.

'Didn't expect to see you here,' Philip said, 'but I'm glad our paths have crossed. Can you spare a moment?'

Bede suppressed a sigh. 'If it's about last week—'

'Not directly. I know I'm not likely to get a confession.'

'Confession?' Bede glanced around. No one was taking the slightest notice except Silvan, who gave him an encouraging grin from his place by the fire. 'This isn't the time or place,' he said quietly, hands forming fists by his side, 'but seeing as you insist, I'd appreciate it if you didn't go around making false insinuations about me.'

Philip smiled unpleasantly. 'So you were careful. I've got my eye on the pair of you.'

Bede uncurled his fingers and willed the tension to flow

out through his fingertips. 'I've got stuff to do, Philip. If that's all…'

'It isn't. You brought that up. Actually, I'd like you to clear your equipment and all your other rubbish out of Holtwood.'

'Yeah? What's it to you?'

'Have you seen Frank recently?'

There was a disconcerting edge to his voice. Neither Bede nor Elin had seen the farmer since the day after the incident, when he'd sounded indignant that anyone had even thought of accusing Bede. He shook his head.

'Oh, I appear to have put my foot in it.' It was obvious Northcote had intended every word. 'I thought he'd have told you by now, sorry. Well, he won't be needing you any more in Holtwood. We're buying it back.' He glanced sideways. 'You've got customers need serving. Talk to Frank. And get your stuff out. I'll give you a couple of weeks but after that I'll have to dispose of it myself.'

He went over to the keepers' table without another word. Bede breathed deeply and made himself concentrate, playing the genial host while suppressing the urge to call Brian through from the kitchen to take over so he could go straight to Frank's and sort it out. Surely he hadn't really caved in to Northcote? It was perfectly obvious he wanted the woodland for additional access to the drilling site, not to mention camouflage, keeping it out of the public eye. Frank had been at the first few protest meetings and in any case, he'd always promised to give the Sherwells first refusal. There was no way they could afford it right now, but still… He tried not to think of heavy machinery churning up the woodland track.

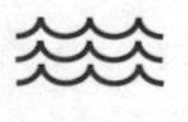

The pub car park was filling up – a typical Friday night. As Elin got out of the car and battled against the blustery rain shower, she wished she hadn't answered the door. She wondered if Frank had been lying in wait for Bede to leave. If so, she liked to think that catching her on her own hadn't spared him much; she could speak her mind as well as her husband when she chose to.

She entered the pub, greeting a couple of people. Behind the bar, Bede was talking cheerfully to Maisie, already looking as if he belonged there. He saw her and smiled. Perhaps she could forget about Frank Barnham, Philip Northcote and Holtwood for a while.

He pulled a pint for her, shaking his head as she offered him one.

'You won't believe who called to see me earlier.' Damn. She hadn't intended to say anything and risk spoiling his first night.

'Frank Barnham,' he said.

It wasn't a question.

'How do you know?'

'Northcote was enjoying a good gloat earlier.' He waved a hand towards the fireplace. She glanced over and saw an empty table. 'Well, that's good news, at least,' he said. 'They've gone. Northcote and his cronies. Including that young bloke, Silvan.'

'He's still here. I saw him as I came in, by the pool table,' Elin said dismissively. 'But what are we going to do about Holtwood?'

Someone was waving a tenner and yelling 'Over here' in his direction. He gave a barely perceptible sigh.

'Sorry, love. We'd best talk about it later. But it seems like there's not a lot we can do.'

He never ceased to surprise her. She could sense his anger

simmering beneath the surface, but it was rare he even attempted to hide it like this.

She went over to join Carole and a group of regulars, and immediately got drawn into a fiercely-fought game of dominoes. It was good to be distracted. Trying not to brood, she let the clacking of the doms and the gentle chatter soothe her.

'Bloody self-righteous creep!'

Elin and Carole exchanged glances as a young girl shoved past them, stumbling on her way back from the bar to join a small crowd around the pool table who were getting louder as the evening went on.

'Isn't that Kate's Tamsin?' Carole said.

Elin nodded as her neighbour's sixteen-year-old daughter pushed her way onto a tiny space on the bench, ignoring two empty seats on the other side of the small table and the protests of the bench's other occupants. She sidled up too obviously close to Silvan, protesting all the while.

'Said didn't I think I'd had enough? And he asked my age! Like, no one does that round here, do they? Maisie always serves me.'

'Hey, chill your beans.' Silvan made to rise. 'I'll get them in for you.'

He stood, clearly escaping. When he returned with a tray of drinks, he caught Elin watching and gave her a fleeting smile.

'I meant to say, hope you enjoyed your birthday last week,' he said cheerfully.

Elin smiled back with some comment about his music. She felt vaguely sorry for him, sitting with a crowd of kids for the sake of a game of pool; he must only be a few years older than them but his confident air set him worlds apart. She almost called him over to their table, but after observing him for a moment decided he was quite capable of joining them himself if he wanted to.

She won her hand of dominoes and enjoyed swirling the clacking stones around the table top in readiness for a new game. Tamsin was making a bit of a fool of herself around Silvan, and Elin winced at her increasingly desperate attempts to get noticed as the night went on.

At the end of the evening, Elin paused in the porch on her way out, to breathe a draught of the night air before venturing out into the rain. Distant voices punctuated by an occasional raucous laugh drifted towards her, and in the glow of the streetlights she saw the group from the pool table making their untidy way home. After a hearty round of goodbyes from inside, Bede joined her and they hurried over to the car. Elin glanced at his bike locked up under cover, and led him firmly past it.

'Yes, I came in the car,' she said defiantly. 'Don't start.'

'Start what?'

'I needed to get out, I wanted to support you on your first night, it's pissing down, and what do you make the biodiesel for anyway?'

She paused, waited for a reaction. He merely held his hand out, palm up. 'I'll drive home if you like, love. I've had less to drink than you have.'

She handed the key over; she had to admit he was right. Rain drummed on the roof and the windows were impenetrably steamed up. Bede started the engine and turned the blower on full. Elin tried to suppress her impatience; her hands were itching to grab a cloth, but it wasn't worth the argument – he always said wiping it left streaks worse than the mist itself. As they waited for the windows to clear he stretched, untied his hair and shook it out over his shoulders.

'That's better.' He smiled at her warmly. 'I wasn't going to say anything, you know. I saw the car when I took some crates out back. Don't blame you, it's a pig of a night.'

He leaned over and drew her to him. The overhead light went out as they kissed.

'Sorry I was snappy,' she said. 'Let's get home.'

A patch of the windscreen had cleared, big enough to see a deserted country lane through, and he set off, stopping as soon as they pulled out of the car park.

'Isn't that Tamsin?' he said.

He indicated a huddled figure in the old brick bus-shelter by the bridge. She'd vaguely wondered how the girl was going to get home. It was less than a mile, but in this weather? Bede wound the window down.

'No buses at this time of night, love. Can we give you a lift?'

The girl raised her head with a look of relief, which vanished as soon as she saw who it was. Panda-eyed with smudged mascara, she waved him away, got unsteadily to her feet and staggered a few steps. Her thin summer dress was soaked; she must be frozen. She halted, sank to her knees and threw up in the gutter. As she tried to rise, she almost overbalanced. Elin got out of the car.

'Come on, let's get you home.'

'Gerroff my case.'

She managed to stand and walked off. An uneven kerbstone tripped her and Elin was there to catch her arm. Tamsin allowed herself to be ushered into the back seat, then slammed the door, making the car shake.

'You!' Tamsin spat the word, glaring at Bede, who did a theatrical double-take.

'Yup. I was last time I looked in a mirror.'

'Whaddya have to, like, show me up in front of my mates for? Who d'you think you are, my fuckin' dad?'

He put the car in gear. 'You've seen the signs behind the bar. No one wants any trouble. Anyway, it might mean you'll have a slightly less pounding hangover tomorrow morning.'

'Keep your nose out, fascist. I'm puffeck...capable of walking, y'know.'

'Yeah, course, but no one wants to be out in rain like this, do they?' he said as he drove off.

Tamsin sank back into the seat, energy spent, and the rest of the short journey passed in silence.

'Mum'll go ballistic,' she said as she fumbled for the door catch.

'If you tiptoe in she'll never know,' Elin said. 'We won't say anything – we've all been there. Get straight to bed and you'll have sobered up by the morning.'

'I'm not drunk now.'

Elin and Bede exchanged glances. As if to prove it, Tamsin flung open the door and got out with all the dignity she could muster.

''S not your fault,' she said, setting off on unsteady legs up her drive.

'Magnanimous, I'm sure,' Bede muttered as he turned the car.

By the time they got home, the rain had eased and they stood for a moment on the Alderleat yard, arms round each other, letting the breeze ruffle their hair as they gazed out across the field to the river. The moon was even venturing out from behind a cloud.

'Did you see what I saw?' Elin said.

'Depends what you saw.'

She could just make out his features in the weak moonlight.

'Philip Northcote's SUV on Kate's drive.'

He laughed. 'At this time of night? Now there's a match made in heaven.'

'Or hell,' they both said together, and laughed.

'He said he intended to keep an eye on us,' Bede said. 'The lengths some people will go to…'

She didn't feel like laughing for long. 'Seriously, though, what about Holtwood?'

'Nothing we can do. We've got nothing to make a counter-offer with.'

'What's got into you tonight?' She sighed. 'We could try and talk Frank round. I can't believe he intends to sell to Northcote of all people! He knows what he wants it for.'

'It won't make any difference to whether or not the test drilling goes ahead. There's no point mithering over what we can't change.'

'You're glad, aren't you? Holtwood's another place that's haunted by Joe and you're only too ready to walk away.'

She wished she could take the words back, but once again he surprised her.

'I won't deny it's a responsibility we can do without,' he said simply. 'But I wouldn't have wished it.'

'Do you think Marjorie knows?'

He shrugged. 'Nothing she could do if she did. She sold Holtwood to Frank fair and square, like she sold this place to Joe. Philip may be her son but he doesn't take any notice of her. We've just got to accept it. I'm as pissed off as you are but you've said yourself there are some things we have to let go.'

How could he be so calm?

'Listen, Elin, I don't want to fight all the time. I will if I have to, when it's important, but I…I think we should let this one go.' He turned to her. 'Maybe that business with the vandalism has shaken me. And you know what, I really enjoyed myself this evening.'

She hugged him. Frustration simmered inside her, but after all, he mattered to her more than Holtwood and it was actually a relief to see him like this. Maybe some things were worth letting go.

Breathing new life

Bede glanced up from the laptop screen as the phone interrupted his train of thought. He smiled. Elin always claimed she didn't have a telephone voice but he loved to hear it. She relaxed into her normal tones and he gathered it was Marjorie. He turned from his spreadsheet, took his glasses off and polished them, listening and suppressing guilt: they hadn't been to see their old friend for a few weeks – not since Philip had moved next door to his mother, into an apartment newly converted from a couple of outbuildings. It sounded like Elin was putting their absence right. She called over to him and he agreed to go and look at her temperamental old solid-fuel central heating boiler – again.

'Honestly, that man.' Elin put the phone down and came to sit across from him.

'Philip? What's he done now?'

'Marjorie's had to huddle up in front of the living room fire for days waiting for him to get someone he knows to see to the central heating. She suggested he call us but apparently you're incompetent, as evidenced by the fact that it's broken down again, and undesirable – which of course doesn't need evidence. But Philip's out this morning.'

Bede had been recommending for years that she get a new system, but as long as he could patch it up she was happy for him to do so, saying that scrapping it would be a waste and therefore a greater evil than the fuel it used. Bede wasn't convinced, but he respected Marjorie's 'waste not, want not' philosophy – an attitude she and Joe had shared. Whatever the boiler's ability to take another weld, maybe he should sign its death certificate this time, help her out by offering to install a biomass boiler like theirs. They could supply her with the willow chippings for next to nothing, shaving more off the carbon footprint by keeping it local.

It would certainly piss Philip off – they suspected he was dying to get his hands on his mother's rambling old farmhouse and rip the heart out of it, for himself or as a money-making exercise, so he'd doubtless consider a new central heating system an expensive irrelevance. Bede smiled grimly. Marjorie had no intention of moving or dying any time soon so he would feel not the slightest guilt in at least discussing it with her.

Before going to Bridge Farm, they called at the Foxover Storehouse and Elin saw Kate browsing the shelves. She'd almost managed to reach the door when her neighbour called out.

'Elin! Can I have a word, please?'

Aware of Bede waiting in the car outside, she tried to think of an excuse, but Kate launched in without giving her the chance. 'I'd be grateful if you could ask your husband to show a little more responsibility around the teenagers. He may think it's amusing, or cool, but I really don't appreciate him encouraging underage girls to drink. What was he thinking of? Even you've got to admit, Elin—'

'Kate, please! I was there on Friday night. Didn't Tamsin tell you? Bede made himself unpopular by refusing to serve her. I have no idea what makes you think he'd encourage her, but—'

'So how come—'

'Someone could have bought drinks for her?'

'Well, he should have kept an eye on the situation.'

'I don't think she even had that much; it just went to her head. And I'll tell you something else: we stopped on the way home – Bede did, actually; he was driving – and we gave her a lift to make sure she got back safely.'

'Oh.' Kate's expression softened, but only for a moment. 'If only he'd been as thoughtful when it came to the drinks. But… Well… Honestly, Elin, it *is* a worry. I admit I sometimes get distracted, running the bed and breakfast on my own. You can't imagine—'

'Don't get me wrong; I do sympathise.' Elin forced a smile, eager to avoid any veiled references to her own lack of parenting experience. 'We'll try and keep an eye on her whenever either of us is in the Horseshoes. OK?' She glanced through the window at their car, saw Bede tapping the wheel impatiently. 'I'm sorry, Kate, but we've got to be getting on.'

The last thing any of them needed was for him to join them for a more acrimonious re-run.

As they pulled into the Bridge Farm yard, Elin's heart sank as she saw Philip's SUV outside the converted outbuildings now called The Grange, not so much parked as sprawled at an angle of casual arrogance. 'Marjorie said he'd be out.'

'Don't worry, he probably is. You don't expect the poor bugger to slum it with just one car, do you?' Bede pulled up neatly parallel to Marjorie's hatchback.

Marjorie had said they should go straight in, and there was a note in the porch confirming it. Elin glanced at Bede but he was opening the sturdy front door before she'd finished reading it. Despite the countless times they'd been there over the years, she still felt like a visitor while he seemed completely at home – an even more unlikely friend to Marjorie than Joe had been. As they stepped into the dusty hallway, Bede called out, his voice fading to the familiar sound of the grandfather clock ticking away the minutes like the heartbeat of the house it presided over. Marjorie's welcoming response drifted through from the back.

Enveloped by the distinctive old-house mustiness, they made for the conservatory. Elin noticed the living-room fire had not yet been raked out and laid. On the coffee table beside the fireplace, the photo of Joe in hiking gear stood where it always had, its frame now draped with his old familiar scarf. She smiled to herself at the fondness it revealed, looking so at home among the jumble of artefacts that crowded the room, documenting Marjorie's travels to destinations that must have been all the more exotic to the sheltered daughter of a Foxover landowner. She wondered if Philip ever thought about his mother's choice to display Joe's photo like that – the framed family portraits on the wall, though larger and grander, seemed more dutiful than affectionate.

Marjorie was where they most often found her, in her beloved winter garden. She spent a lot of time looking out over the cheerful colour of the flower beds towards the river, enjoying the room's apparent knack of drawing in sunshine even on a dull day. Joe had spent many an afternoon patching up leaks in the conservatory roof until eventually he and Bede had insisted on reglazing it for her – the kind of favour they had always done without question.

As she stood to welcome them, a hint of distance and guilt in Marjorie's expression suggested she'd been dozing. She was immediately enveloped in a bear hug from Bede.

He dwarfed her at the best of times, but to Elin this seemed the first time she'd actually looked her eighty years. She hugged her in turn and kissed her marshmallow cheek. Marjorie announced that the kettle was on and must have boiled by now.

'Tea all round?' Bede disappeared in the direction of the kitchen.

'The biscuits are in the tin,' Marjorie called after him.

Elin sat in the chair Marjorie indicated, breathing in the wisps of fresh spring breeze that carried a little of the outdoors through an open window into the sun-warmed conservatory.

'You're looking well, my dear,' Marjorie said. She lowered her voice. 'And what about that young man of yours?'

'Bede's fine, thanks.'

'Really? You know you don't have to hide anything from me.'

'Really.' Elin smiled. 'There's nothing to hide.'

'It's good to hear it. Joe's passing hit him so hard. I'm glad he's coming out of it – I was only pleased he felt he could talk to me when he needed to.' She frowned slightly. 'Not that I didn't realise, you understand, and try and get him to talk to you.'

'I'm sure. It's fine.' She'd never confessed to anyone, not even Fran, her bouts of insane jealousy during those months that he'd opened up to Marjorie, or even Joe's bloody dog, rather than express his feelings to her.

'I know he sometimes felt guilty about taking you for granted.' Marjorie took her hand and squeezed it. 'So has he finally accepted it was an accident?'

'Come to terms with the fact he's never going to prove otherwise. We're fine now, honestly. Did you know Brian's got him working at the Horseshoes?'

'Now that I do find hard to imagine.'

Relieved at the change of subject, they both smiled, and reminisced about when Marjorie used to go to the pub regularly with Joe. Her favourite seat by the inglenook fireplace had always cleared as if by magic; even visitors somehow seemed to know it was hers.

Bede returned with the tea-tray – two cups and saucers and a mug – and found a place for it among the clutter on the side-table. Elin poured as he handed the plate of biscuits round before taking the mug and perching on a footstool.

'Now then.' Marjorie turned to Bede, a slight tremor in her hand rattling the cup in the saucer as she picked it up. 'Is it true what I heard about you having a go at Philip's new venture? The pheasant pens in Holtwood?'

Her voice was stern, but her veiled smile suggested she certainly didn't back her son in all he did, and might even approve of the end if not the means. Bede held his hands up.

'First I knew about it was when I was wrongly accused.'

'Really?'

'Oh, come off it!' His tone made Elin flinch, but as so often she was amazed by what Marjorie would tolerate from him. 'Do you really think I'd stoop so low as to harm innocent birds?'

His eyes sparked with challenge and amusement.

'Remember who you're talking to, young man.' Marjorie shook her head in mock disapproval. 'Just take care. Though maybe my son's activities in and around the woods *have* gone far enough. I've made it clear what I think.'

Elin knew Holtwood still had a special place in Marjorie's heart despite the years that had passed since she'd sold it. Any pleasure she might have at Philip buying it back was clearly fragile. The allusion she'd just made was as close as she'd ever come to speaking directly about the fracking proposals, however, and even Bede had agreed it was wise not to push her.

'Don't tell me he should be looking closer to home for the culprit?' he said. Elin held her breath.

'Enough.' Marjorie's voice was playful but her expression warned him not to take it too far.

'Well, if you girls will excuse me.'

Bede stood, topped up his tea and left to see to the boiler.

'Philip's still convinced it's him.' Marjorie gave Elin a long, searching look. She didn't reply; even if she had her own doubts, she certainly wouldn't betray them to anyone else. 'Though I believe the pair of you,' Marjorie continued. 'Bede rarely does anything without good reason. Not like Joe.' She gazed out of the window. 'He was a good man, but...' Elin savoured that rare 'but' to what she sometimes couldn't help thinking of as the cult of Joe. 'I always thought he seemed a bit lost. Only came here to get away. He needed that; I was glad I could let the place to him. But I think he'd have happily allowed Alderleat to crumble round his ears as he pottered in the garden. Who'd have thought it would be your Bede... Used to roar up on that great beast of a motorcycle – you remember that?'

Elin smiled, recalling the heady mix of terror and exhilaration she'd got from riding pillion on their early dates. After he'd become more involved at Calsthorpe and then Alderleat, he'd suddenly sold his beloved Triumph. Just like that: from one day to the next it became part of his past. He simply claimed that shedding the bike was as important a part of his personal development as anything he'd ever learned about its mechanics.

'I found him a little intimidating at first, if you don't mind me saying,' Marjorie continued. Elin smiled in sympathy. 'No manners, the lines of his hands always black with oil as if to declare there was no point cleaning them properly because time spent away from making or repairing something was time wasted. Who'd have thought he'd ever come to live here?' She turned from the window to look at Elin. 'We've got you to thank for that. Meeting you certainly changed him for the better.'

Elin laughed. 'Once Joe had persuaded him to actually speak to me.'

Her frustration had almost bordered on contempt as Bede had failed to respond to her, until the day he'd hesitantly asked her to go with him into the Calsthorpe trees, hunting mushrooms. Whether or not the invitation had been down to Joe's matchmaking, his knowledge of edible fungi and the vast underground mycelium networks, and his enthusiasm for sharing it with her, seemed to open a floodgate, and soon they were talking naturally as if they'd always known each other.

'Oh, he used to play the sullen young man with me, too,' Marjorie said. 'But the way he confided in Joe, I could see there was heart beneath the surface. It was a slow process but I warmed to him. And I know Joe was thrilled when the two of you agreed to come and live here.'

'It was the perfect opportunity for us to put our ideas into practice,' Elin said. She would never, especially not after Joe's untimely death, voice the occasional longing she'd felt for her and Bede to have a place of their own.

'More than that. Joe liked having family around him,' Marjorie said as though she'd read her mind.

'Likewise, you must be pleased that Philip's come to live next door.'

'I thought it was only temporary, while he settled down after the divorce and got on with renovating the Grange. I assumed he intended to sell it or let it out when it was finished, but it looks like he's staying.' She sighed almost imperceptibly. 'He seems to think I need looking after, though I think I'm putting him right on that score.' She smiled at Elin. 'At least we've each got our own front door.'

As he came through from the boiler room in the lobby connecting Marjorie's kitchen and Philip's front door, Bede tried to deny the nerves he always felt here. That time he'd turned up at Bridge Farm looking for Joe, the Grange had still been a ramshackle outbuilding and Marjorie's kitchen its timeless self. Hearing raised, angry voices – his uncle's and one he didn't recognise – he'd paused outside the half-open back door.

'I'm telling you to drop it, clear off and stay away.'

'It may disappoint you, but there are some things in this world you can't control.' Joe's voice had an edge Bede had rarely heard. 'Not your mother and certainly not me.'

At the harsh sound of chairs scraping the flagged floor, Bede had raised his hand and knocked as if he'd just that moment arrived. A middle-aged man, whom he now knew to be Philip, snatched open the door, glared at him, then turned back to Joe.

'If you insist on going ahead, I swear you'll regret it.'

They'd gone ahead with buying out the Alderleat lease and hadn't regretted a thing over the years, but how long could the man's grudge last? Of course Bede had reported the conversation after Joe's death, but even he could see that an unsubstantiated memory was hardly evidence. And surely the fracking proposals weren't personal.

Shaking his head, he turned back to the task in hand.

Satisfied everything was working, he moved to the fireplace, ready to put the back boiler and the whole creaky system to the test. A match to the crumpled newspapers brought the flames to life and he relished watching the *Daily Mail* burn. He fed the fire, feeling dirty as he did so, but it needed coal to run properly. As the initial roar settled to a steady crackle, he allowed his gaze to be drawn by the glow, and thought again that he really must have a word with her about renewing it.

Don't you start. She's got enough on with Philip telling her what to do.

He started, looked around. I'm only trying to help.

She'll ask when she's ready. No need to cause trouble between her and that son of hers.

Bede glanced accusingly at the fire, then quickly swept up. He went back through to the boiler room and checked the tank – at least he'd made sure that it was well lagged – and the pump, observing it all with the satisfaction of a job well done, tinkering with a few adjustments. He heard a key in the lock of the adjacent porch, followed by Philip's voice. 'Hello? Someone there?'

As Bede removed his glasses and wiped his hands on his overalls, he reminded himself he had nothing to feel guilty about.

'Well, well. This is a surprise.' Philip declined to shake his grimy hand. 'What are you doing here?'

'Your mother phoned us. Asked me to look at the boiler. She's in the conservatory with Elin.'

So go and have it out with her. Leave me to finish off in peace.

'I've got someone booked in to see to this, the day after tomorrow.'

'No need now.'

Philip glared at him as though Bede's actions were not so much to help his mother as to criticise him. He brought out a leather wallet from his pocket. 'How much do we owe you?'

Bede frowned, genuinely taken aback. 'Owe me?'

'For the repairs.'

'Nothing.'

Philip radiated irritation. The man could even take declining payment as an insult. He strode off towards the conservatory. As Bede heard Marjorie greet her son calmly, he was once again struck by how different they were, and wondered what on earth her late husband must have been like.

11th June 1999

Today was a good day. I've taken a few days' holiday and I'm here in my trusty tent in the mountains for a bit of fishing, bit of time alone in the wild to recharge. First proper time I've spent outdoors since I lost the allotment – all the paperwork for that went home and Suzanne just cancelled the lease out from under me. Well, no point in dwelling on the bad, though I do miss the soil on my hands. Look on the bright side – I met a couple of interesting people earlier.

After an early start, there I was, drinking a coffee from the snack van, when suddenly there's this blare of horns and a movement in my mirror, a hatchback veering off onto the verge. I'm out like a shot, to a last doppler of a horn fading off down the outside lane. Blow-out by the look of it. She did well to get off the road – from the skid marks it looked like she was in the outside lane – but she's sitting there looking shaken, watching me jog up. Shaken but in control. Not bad for a woman in her fifties, sixties maybe. The remnant of tyre was a hazard to traffic so I dived out between cars to retrieve it, and I'm almost as shaken as she is by the time I offer to help change the wheel – though she looks like she'd have been more than capable on her own.

By the time we'd done and I'd bought us a nice calming cuppa and the comfort food of bacon butties, I'd heard all about Marjorie Northcote's beautiful-sounding place in a little village by the River Severn – or maybe it's just her accent makes me think it's something special. Not too cut-glass but quite posh all the same. She's got plans to settle down and sort out her crumbling old house after a few years spent travelling. Said she wanted to do something useful after her husband died and she's been driving across the continent and beyond for charities, delivering aid parcels and the like. Got to admire her.

When she turned to me and said 'Tell me, what does a knight in shining armour do when there are no damsels in distress to rescue?' I confess I felt a bit inadequate. I mean, a hardware shop. I'm proud of how I've built the business up, and I've got some decent skills, but it sounds a bit...unknightly, doesn't it? And there I am spending my weekends on the allotment (well I used to, at least), or going off into the mountains on my own, when she's out there devoting her life to helping people.

Once we were both sure she was OK, she continued on her way to visit her friend, leaving me with an outpouring of eternal gratitude and an invitation to visit. The river Severn. Shropshire. I know nothing about it bar the Welsh borderlands, and aren't there supposed to be blue remembered hills or something?

After waving her off, I was just leaving the layby when I saw a group of hitchers, bloke and two women (lucky sod). A bit scruffy but you don't expect hitchers to be wearing black tie, do you? My half-hour with Marjorie had given me a taste for chatting, I like my own company but after recent weeks you really can have too much of a good thing, so I decided I could squeeze them in, rucksacks & all.

I told them where I was heading and the taller girl with long, wavy red hair just kind of nods and they head for the car. The fella, looked a bit stoned, introduced himself as Tim and shoved his rucksack in the boot before hunkering down on the back seat, too gone-out, knackered or maybe just plain shy to say more. The gypsy-haired girl grins at me all full of fun, like, and simply says 'Fran' as she clambers into the back with the rest of their stuff between them, leaving her mate, really drop-dead gorgeous she is, scowling at me. I think you'd call her a willowy blonde, at least that's what I ended up calling her in my head, Willow (had to stop myself saying it out loud) because there was no move to speak to the likes of me. She finally got in the front, as gracefully as she could while looking down her nose at me. She slammed the door shut as if expecting it not to latch properly and immediately wound the window down.

'Smells of dead pig in here.' Dead quiet she said it, craning round to her mates in the back, as though I'm not meant to hear.

'You mean my bacon butty?' I'm smiling to myself as the embarrassment flits across her face. 'Listen, love, I can find you a piece of cardboard. Just write VEGAN on it and you'll get a lift to suit you in no time, I'm sure.'

I noticed the lass called Fran stifling a laugh.

'Anyway, sooner you belt up, sooner we'll be there and you can get the offensive molecules out your nostrils.'

'I beg your pardon?'

I tapped her seat belt clasp. She rolled her eyes but obeyed, clicking it like it was a gun aimed at an abattoir guy. I saw the ghost of a smile. She was something when she wasn't hiding it behind a veil of self-righteousness. Told myself I'd no chance – they look like students which would make her not much over half my age. Made me feel old all of a sudden, that did, though I really related to them. She didn't look the sort to fancy a bit of rough, but you never know your luck.

It seems they're on their way to some peace camp in a forest in Northumberland. Fran starts telling me, arms waving, how the three of them are second years at Nottingham Uni and regularly go off for a few days to join this guy Graham Scott – Grey – who's got this land, Calsthorpe Wood, that was in his family, and he's got a crowd in there to occupy it because the ancient, once-they're-gone-they're-gone-forever trees are threatened by a road scheme. Yeah, that's right, another one. What's the point, I said, it'll soon become another standing traffic jam, we should be looking to proper public transport. Fran catches my eye in the rearview mirror like she's found a soulmate.

Anyway, they've got a right little community going on there, building shacks out of 'found materials' from mother nature's bounty and living off the land. They're fighting this road through the courts and planning procedures, but if push comes to shove they're dug in ready to protest. Quite sad when you think of what they're doing and it could all be crushed. But much as I sympathise 100% with what they're doing – I actually found myself admiring those tree-dwelling fellas, Swampy and co, on the news a few years ago – it was all getting a bit heavy and I could feel my week on my ownsome in the mountains beckoning.

Except that, when I drop them off, Willow – who turns out to be called Sophie – actually invites me to come & see Calsthorpe Wood for myself on my way home.

Seeing as it's you, love, I might well cut my fishing trip short.

Nice work

On the way home from Marjorie's, Elin dropped Bede off at the pub to collect Brian's car. He arrived shortly afterwards and soon had it up on the ramp beneath the open shelter for a quick assessment before lunch. She let Kip out and before long was immersed in her work in the greenhouse. The gentle hissing of the watering system formed the backdrop to a discussion on the radio she'd lost track of. She started as she became aware that she wasn't alone, turned and was surprised to see Tamsin standing in the doorway.

'Hello,' Elin said with a smile. 'Sorry, you made me jump – I was miles away there. Come on in.'

Tamsin moved to lean on the nearest raised bed.

'Just thought I'd drop by. I'm on my way to the village to post a parcel for Mum. She was about to get the car out again but I said I'd go for her. On my bike.'

She looked at Elin as if seeking approval.

'I saw her in the village earlier. I gather you didn't manage to sneak in last week.'

'Oh my God. What did she say?'

'What you'd expect. Don't worry, I'm not going to lecture you. But it's not a good idea—'

'I know.' The girl's face flushed. 'I've had a whole week of it. She's grounded me, you know. This weekend, too. I'm sick of it. Just had to get out.'

Elin smiled in sympathy then turned back to her plants. 'Can't be easy.'

Tamsin picked a leaf of parsley, started chewing, then pulled a face. 'Made a right prat of myself, didn't I?'

Elin made a non-committal comment about having a good time.

'Don't tell Mum I'm here, yeah? She'd throw a fit. But I just wanted to… Can't remember what I said but… He pissed me off big-time, showing me up in front of my mates. Self-righteous hippy.' Elin looked up from her seed tray, eyebrows raised. 'Like, everyone has a drink in there, there's never any trouble. I was like, would he prefer it if I got out the weed instead?' She glanced around the greenhouse as if searching for evidence. 'Well, anyway, you didn't have to stop, did you? On the way home. I was, y'know, a bit out of order. So, um, thanks. You know? Tell him thanks.'

'Will do.' Elin was tempted to send her to thank him herself. 'A word of advice, though. If you want to get served again – soft drinks of course – you'd be best off not mentioning the H-word.' Tamsin frowned. 'Hippy.'

She grinned. 'Thought you'd take it as a compliment.'

'Apart from hating labels in general, Bede thinks a hippy's little more than a dreamer who sits around getting stoned and romanticising, while he's mister down-to earth, out there actually getting things done.'

'So what's with the wonky fashion sense and the long hair?'

Elin couldn't help laughing. 'Don't you mean absence of fashion sense? Goes with the "labels" thing – fashion's actually the true F-bomb, you know. And brand's the B-word. Unnecessary consumption, excess use of resources – don't get him going. Not that I disagree; so many perfectly decent clothes are just chucked out, and there's plenty of opportunity to get brilliant ones second-hand.'

'I like trawling the charity shops myself. Never thought of it as recycling, just bargain-hunting.' Tamsin held up a hand. 'So don't tell me – he doesn't want to clog up landfill sites with hair clippings.'

'Nice one. It's more…freedom of expression? You'll have to ask him yourself. Personally, I just think it suits him, however impractical it is.' She smiled and ran her hand through her short hair as if to emphasise her point. 'I don't mean to be rude; you can stay as long as you like, but I need to get on.'

'Sure. What're you doing?'

Elin showed her how she was transplanting seedlings. She was surprised when Tamsin pitched in to help, getting soil beneath her carefully manicured fingernails. She was soon absorbed and Elin left her to it, turning to prepare some boxes for the next delivery to Foxover Storehouse. A guest on *Woman's Hour* was talking enthusiastically about her permaculture smallholding. Elin smiled to herself as she thought of Bede agreeing wholeheartedly with the philosophy, lifestyle and community but bemoaning the coining of 'yet another label'. Once her boxes were neatly stacked, she went over to help Tamsin.

'So… I see you've met Silvan.'

'Silvan?' The girl's head was bent to the plants but Elin could see her cheeks were slightly flushed. 'Oh, the new gamekeeper, you mean. Thinks he's God's gift.'

'Know what you mean. Though he's not a bad guitarist. We were in on my birthday and—'

'Yeah, didn't we all know it by the time he'd finished. Plays in some band back in Birmingham. No Surrender. Doesn't sound like my kind of thing, to be honest.' Tamsin straightened. 'Here, I think that's it. Is that OK?'

Elin looked over what she'd done; nodded. Tamsin glanced at her watch.

'Shit! I'd better be off. Shouldn't be here, you know. Listen, before I go, another reason I came – Mum's always on at me to get a job. D'you need any help round here?'

'Loads. But I'm not sure how much we could pay you. I'll have a chat with Bede if you like and—'

As though summoned, he appeared in the greenhouse doorway.

'Have you been in the workshop at all today? I— Oh, hi, Tamsin.'

She smiled uncertainly.

'Me?' Elin said. 'No. What's up?'

'It's just...I think I'm going crazy. I went to get my toolbox – you know, to look at Brian's car and...can't help feeling that stuff's been moved.'

'Post-visitor trauma.' Elin winked at Tamsin. 'We had some friends over last week – you probably saw them – and he's spent the last few days putting things back "where they ought to be".'

Tamsin rolled her eyes. 'I wouldn't have you down as, like, an OCD kind of guy.'

Bede shrugged. 'Guilty as charged. I like things in their proper place.'

'So what have you lost?' Elin said.

'Nothing. I just feel...'

Elin shook her head. 'You feel like you're getting more absent-minded every day and wanted an excuse to see who our visitor is.'

'Don't give away *all* my secrets at once.' He picked up a piece of twine and began to knot it absently. 'Sorry, Tamsin, that wasn't very welcoming, was it? Good to see you. Don't tell me Elin's got you at work already.'

'I was just asking her, actually... You know...Saturday job or whatever.'

‘I’m sure we can sort something out.’ He glanced at Elin.

‘That’d be awesome. Let me know. Look, I’m sorry, but I’ve got to go now.’ As Tamsin headed for the door, Elin gestured pointedly towards Bede. ‘I only came to…like… thank you. For the lift the other night.’

He nodded with a hint of amusement. ‘You’re welcome.’

‘Well, see you later.’

Bede watched her pick up her bike and pedal off.

‘Was it something I said?’

‘It’s not all about you, you know.’ Elin smiled and went over to him. ‘Though you wouldn’t believe it to hear Marjorie talk.’

‘What’s that supposed to mean?’

She smiled. ‘Your number one fan. I’m surprised your ears weren’t burning enough to heat the water in that boiler.’

‘Tell me more.’

‘Over lunch.’ She headed for the door. ‘Not that there’s much to tell. You, on the other hand, can give me the story of what Philip said to make you so eager to leave.’

‘It wasn’t so much what *he* said. More a case of walking away before *I* said something I’d regret.’

She knew he wasn’t joking.

As she cycled to the village, Tamsin felt pleased with herself. Not only had she got the excruciating embarrassment of last Friday night out of the way relatively painlessly, but she had the prospect of a job. Nice work, she told herself – far more interesting than the shop counters or delivery rounds most of her friends had, and certainly better than skivvying in the B&B for her mum, who as often as not forgot to give her the pocket money she’d earned. She got the impression

Bede didn't really want her around. Not that he'd said anything; there was just something about him. But she was confident Elin could persuade him. She'd never really understood what her mum had against their neighbours – her prejudice reason enough for Tamsin to like them from afar – but would never have imagined herself getting involved.

She might earn less than Lauren and her other mates, but it would be enough and it was local. Most possible Saturday jobs would be town-based, and her mum, keen to get her out of the house since Philip had been on the scene, would be bound to suggest she spent more time at her dad's. That would mean weekends away from her mates and the Horseshoes, now with the added attraction of... She told herself not to even go there. She didn't stand a chance.

As she entered the post office, her heart did a small somersault as she saw Silvan's artfully spiky hair and dark eyes across the shop. It sank to her boots when she saw he was talking to Lauren and chatting up Megan Shaw. Typical. She might not stand a chance, but didn't need the evidence right in front of her. She paused, wondering if she could reach the counter without being noticed. Too late. Lauren beckoned her across.

'Hey!' Tamsin walked over, all outward confidence. Silvan actually smiled, but her pleasure was immediately deflated when Megan opened her mouth.

'If it isn't the Cider Queen.'

'What's that supposed to mean?' Tamsin said, hating herself for rising to it.

'Oh, nothing.' The older girl grinned. 'Well, I can't hang around. See you guys in the Shoes tonight.' She looked directly at Silvan as she said it, then turned to Tamsin. 'Silvan's going to bring his guitar. You coming?'

'Can't, sorry.' She wished she could think of a decent excuse. Lauren would understand, but she bet Silvan had never been grounded in his life, and would have walked brazenly out of the house if he had.

To her relief, Megan didn't push it, but her departure broke up the little group. Lauren joined Tamsin in the post-office queue for a moment of sympathising, before going on her way. Tamsin realised she'd been too distracted to tell her about Alderleat. She'd also managed to say nothing to Silvan except *Hey* and *Bye*. No wonder she didn't stand a chance.

On her way out of the village, she was changing gear for the hump-backed bridge when something clanked and the pedals whirred emptily. Shit. The chain had come off – again. She leaned it against the bridge wall, grabbed a dock leaf to keep her fingers clean and tried to coax the filthy chain back onto the cog, but to no avail. Her kid brother Simon was the expert, but she had to get the stupid thing home first. With a weary sigh, she started pushing.

She hadn't gone far before a jeep pulled up beside her.

'Can I help?'

The voice made her treacherous heart race.

'D'you know anything about bikes?'

'Not really. I can give you a lift, though.' Without waiting for a reply, Silvan jumped out and stowed the bike effortlessly in the back among some sacks of seed and a clanking assortment of gear. 'Hop in.'

Tamsin obeyed in a flash, feeling slightly disappointed that there was no one around to see her. They set off in an embarrassing silence as she desperately tried to think of something cool to say. He slowed by Holtwood and asked if she minded a quick detour to drop the sacks off at the pens before he took her home.

'No problem.'

'You sure you can't come tonight?' he said as he negotiated the rutted track. 'Is it anything to do with last week?'

Shit, he'd noticed. 'What...?'

He flashed her a smile. 'Lauren told me. Nothing to be ashamed of, getting grounded. Part of growing up. My folks were really strict too, you know. Couldn't wait to leave, get my own place – it'll come before you know it – but, you know, now I have, there are times I actually miss them.'

They reached the pheasant pens and he drew to a halt. 'Did you get home all right the other night?'

Did he have to pile on the embarrassment? 'Sure. My neighbours gave me a lift.'

'Bede and Elin?'

'Yeah.' He knew them. And he was interested enough to know where she lived. Things were looking up.

He waved towards the pheasant pens. 'I suppose you heard about the vandalism here. Do you think it was him – Bede?'

'Dunno.' She'd heard her mum going on about it several times, vowing to get her free-range eggs and organic produce for the B&B elsewhere from now on. She was probably only trying to impress Philip. Tamsin herself had hardly given it a second thought, but now found herself siding with her new friends. 'I doubt it.'

'Who else do you think it could have been, then?'

She looked across at him. Surely he didn't suspect her? 'No idea.'

'Can't be easy having Philip around the house.'

Shit, *that*. 'I keep out the way as much as I can.'

She was reluctant to say too much about his employer until she knew more about his own opinion.

'Don't blame you. So, how well do you know the Sherwells?'

'A bit. You know.' He nodded, clearly waiting for her to go on. 'We moved to Bankside about twelve years ago. I think they'd been there a couple of years before that. So I've seen them around, like, for ever. I help out there now.' No need to tell him she'd spent half an hour there so far and was merely hoping for more regular work.

'They seem interesting – all that green sustainability stuff.' He raised his eyebrows. 'Not that I buy into it myself. Don't get me wrong, I respect what they're doing, of course, but no one's going to tell me that undoing technology and going back to a more primitive age is the answer.'

'But they're not—'

'There are plenty of resources to keep us going in our lifetime and beyond, and people will have thought of a proper solution by the time Armageddon arrives. In the meantime, we're not gonna cope with change if the economy goes tits-up.'

As she was trying to find the words to protest, he jumped out of the jeep. 'Work to do. Won't be long.'

He dragged a couple of sacks from the back, jolting her bike alarmingly, stacked them by the fence and topped up the grain hopper at the edge of the pheasant pen. Tamsin pushed her disapproval aside and simply enjoyed watching him. He disappeared into the pen and she turned to gaze beyond the clearing into the undergrowth beneath gently swaying branches. The smell of wild garlic reminded her of how they used to come and play in Holtwood when they were kids, making dens and laying treasure hunts for one another. Lauren's brother had even set up a rope swing out over the river one time. It was mad that she hadn't been to the woods for so long. She glanced at the pheasant pens and the glimpse beyond of fields threatened with drilling in some future that felt unreal to her. They'd probably start restricting access before long.

Silvan reappeared and climbed in.

'Listen, Tammy, if you can't make it tonight, how about getting together tomorrow?' he said as he started the jeep and they moved away. 'I've got a day off.'

He glanced over with a smile that, together with that *Tammy*, made her heart leap and convinced her that she could sneak or argue her way out of the house during daylight hours.

'Yeah, that'd be great.' Common sense made a brief appearance. 'I'm not sure how long for, though.'

'No problem. We don't have to go far – we could just go for a walk or whatever. Did you know there's a water vole burrow on the opposite bank?' He pointed back over his shoulder.

'I thought they'd gone,' Tamsin said. 'You know, since the floods.' She realised with a touch of regret that she had no idea whether the floods had driven them away; maybe it was more the case that she'd lost interest in nature and the outdoors over recent years.

'I've seen them all right. I could bring us a snack and some bottles. We can stay for as long as you like.'

'Awesome.'

They arranged to meet, out of sight on the path through the woods, and swapped phone numbers in case bad weather meant changing the arrangements. At Bankside, he jumped out, went round to the back and hoisted her bike out. She thanked him for the lift.

'See you tomorrow,' she said, trying to keep her voice casual.

The finer things in life

'You want to see it, Eco!'

'Believe me, Mikey, I don't.' Bede put the last glass on the shelf, folded the teatowel and hung it to dry. 'Now, what can I get you?'

'Pint of Seven Bells, please. Oh, come on. Even you can't be such a killjoy. It's not every day—'

'No? There's some hope left for the world, then.' He smiled as he put the pint on the bar. 'How's Janet?'

As Mikey chatted about his wife's progress after her recent operation, Bede wished it was as easy to deflect everyone's interest. So Northcote had got himself a Bentley. On top of everything else it was just such a cliché.

A small group came in, Brian among them. He came round to Bede's side of the bar.

'I can take over for a moment or two if you want to go and have a look.'

Bede merely raised an eyebrow.

'Know your enemy?' Brian said.

'I know it as well as I want to, thanks.' Or did he mean the man?

'Whatever your views,' Mikey said, 'surely you want to have a look? She's a sight for sore eyes.'

'Beauty's in the eye of the beholder,' Bede said.

Brian grinned. 'Your Elin's eyes must work in a mighty unique way.'

Bede made a show of flicking a speck of dust from his Horseshoes T-shirt – the first new garment he'd had in a while. 'I've no idea what you're talking about.'

'Seriously, though,' Brian said, 'I'd have thought you'd show some interest. There's a piece of engineering perfection standing out there and you're too stubborn to go and look.'

'Useful purpose is an essential aspect of engineering perfection.'

Mikey rolled his eyes. 'I'd give up if I were you, Bri. You can't expect Eco to join in a bit of harmless fun.'

'Since when has fucking up the planet been harmless?' His voice was casual, playful even, but Brian flashed him a warning look. Bede ignored him. 'The only thing harmless about those things is that most people can't afford them.'

Shaking his head, Mikey went off towards the pool table.

'Lighten up, hey?' Brian said as they watched him go.

Bede raised his eyebrows. 'Don't want to disappoint my audience. I hate to think you're falling at his feet just because—'

'I'm not, but I've got a business to run. And he brings a few customers through the door.'

It wasn't long before Philip Northcote came through the door himself.

'I've been hearing great things about your new motor.' Bede reached for Philip's personal glass and began to pull his usual pint.

'You surprise me.'

'Oh?'

'Didn't have you down as the fawning kind.'

'Blow me. Now I'm being criticised for trying to be polite. Actually, I said "hearing" great things. As a thinking man, I don't always agree with everything I hear. So tell me more, like how many miles per gallon does she do?'

Philip leaned on the bar. 'If you need to ask you can't afford it.'

'You know perfectly well where I'm coming from. Doesn't it make you feel dirty, like you're trailing a huge cloud of poison and particulates behind you?'

'Oh, change the bloody record. I'm all for emission controls, bla bla, if it keeps you lot happy. She complies with all the legislation. Though I remain to be convinced it has anything to do with a bit of unsettled weather. Tell you what, I'll park her up in the garage for a few weeks and we'll enjoy perfect spring sunshine, watch the river levels drop.' Bede refused to rise to the bait. 'Whatever you think, surely you've got to stop every now and then to appreciate the finer things in life. Isn't that what civilisation's all about?'

Bede handed him his pint. 'I guess we'll just have to agree to differ on what constitutes "civilisation" and "the finer things in life".'

Philip looked at him as though Bede wouldn't know a fine thing if it kicked him up the arse, then paid for his drink and went to sit down.

'I could listen to you two all night,' Brian said with a wink.

A little later, Bede collected his cue from the store and went through to the pool room, giving a smile and a nod to his team mates. He settled down for a few moments' practice before they set off for the game. The combination of precision and tactics suited him. He had no illusions about what they thought of him most of the time, but he was their best player and they respected him for that, at least. Winning hearts and minds with a game of pool; everyone had to start somewhere.

He potted a few balls, pleased to find he was on form. Looking up, he realised Silvan had joined the small group. He was becoming quite the fixture.

'New team member?' Bede asked as he walked over.

Gareth nodded. 'We're a bit short tonight. Jack's working away and Mikey doesn't want to go to an away game because he needs to be home early for Janet. Silvan's stepping in.'

'Welcome on board,' Bede said. 'D'you play much?'

'A bit – nothing special. I'm just helping out. On the other hand, I've heard you're a bit of a star.' He smiled, then peered at Bede's cue. 'Joe Sherwell. Is that your late uncle?'

Bede held it out for Silvan to take a closer look. They'd bought it for Joe and had it engraved with his name for Christmas one year. 'My pride and joy – he taught me all I know about the game.'

'Nice.' Silvan ran his finger appreciatively along the wood, before looking up at him. 'That uncle of yours meant a lot to you, didn't he?'

Bede frowned. 'Of course.'

'Joe's sorely missed by us all,' Gareth said. 'Come on, lads, we'd better be off. Don't want to be late.'

'Can someone ride with me?' Silvan said. 'Make sure I don't get lost.'

'We're taking my car tonight,' Gareth said.

'OK, I'll follow you. Don't mind giving someone a lift, though.'

'We're all going in Gareth's,' Bede said. 'Unless you can fit everyone in yours?'

Silvan frowned. 'I doubt it.'

'So it makes sense to take Gareth's. We all chip in for the petrol; it's perfectly fair. Just one lot of petrol.'

'And Eco doesn't like soiling his hands paying for that. I hope that electric car of yours, when it materialises, is going to be a people carrier.' Gareth winked at Bede, turned back to Silvan. 'But most importantly,' he continued, 'team spirit. We all go together.'

Willow withies lay scattered around the kitchen table in a tangle. Elin paused, momentarily tracing their random patterns before returning to the tamed lines of the half-formed basket base at her fingertips. Her hands took over as her mind wandered. It was like the random patterns of life – paths crossing, threads interweaving.

She turned up the stakes to form the sides, her attention drawn to the rain drumming relentlessly on the windows and roof. Disturbing her quiet music indoors, making a mire of the yard outside, keeping her from the garden and seeping dampness into the house, it was making her feel uneasy. She'd felt like this since their visit to Marjorie. Or maybe she'd felt like this since Philip – with all that he brought with him – had come back to live permanently in Foxover. Bede had scoffed about Philip's incredulity when he refused payment, muttering about a world where nothing happened without money changing hands. Elin wondered if there were more to it than that: a reference to his mother selling them Alderleat so cheaply, as though by doing her enough favours they might be angling for a share of Bridge Farm. It would be laughable if the man weren't so serious. As for his activities in Holtwood, she shuddered to think he might have his sights set on similarly reclaiming Alderleat.

She thought again about the vandalism, feeling a flash of anger at whoever had done it. It could even have been what goaded Philip into buying the woodland and keeping them out. No, people didn't make business decisions on such a flimsy basis. And anyway, why blame Bede? Her fingers paused in their weaving. She'd defend him to the hilt in public, but couldn't help wondering. No smoke without fire. A notion flashed into her mind – they'd just been talking about Fran and Jeff's news when he left. Perhaps he'd anticipated the conversation it was bound to lead to, and it was some perverse way of proving he was an unfit dad. He'd done stranger things. She gave herself a mental shake. What on earth was she thinking? She sat back and checked over the evenness of her growing basket.

Kip gave a small, sharp bark as a vehicle on the yard made itself heard above the noise of the weather. She put the basket down and peered out of the window. The colourful Sunny Days logo stood out faintly on the side of the van, incongruous in the streaming rain. She opened the door to Steve Day's cheery smile, light brown mop of hair and characteristic bright tribal-patterned jacket.

'Elin!'

He enfolded her in a hug that was a little too enthusiastic, lingered a little too long. She ushered him in out of the rain.

'Good to see you. What brings you here?'

'Sorry, should've phoned. Never quite got the chance.' He launched into an unnecessarily detailed description of his route and the day's events. 'So I was in the area and thought I'd drop by. I've got a job that might interest Bede.'

'I'm afraid he won't be back for a while. Sit down, though, have a drink.' She waved him to a chair at the kitchen table and put the kettle on. 'Coffee? Tea?' His pause was perfectly pitched to make her add, 'Something stronger?'

He had a knack for it. She was flicking the kettle switch off and heading for the utility room off the kitchen, where she kept her beer, almost before he replied.

'How is he?' Steve asked.

'Great,' she said, flicking him a wary glance before

pouring the beers. 'He's working tonight – teatime shift, then they were off to a pool match.'

'Working?'

'He's been playing mine host at the Horseshoes for a couple of weeks now.'

Steve's lips curled in amusement. 'You've got to be joking.'

'He's better at it than you'd think. Even manages to be nice to the customers – when it suits him.'

They exchanged a smile. Steve gingerly moved aside some withies to put his glass down.

'He…he'll be OK with me coming here?'

'I never told him, if that's what you mean.'

Elin was convinced Bede had suspected nothing in his fog of self-absorption during the months following Joe's death. She'd woken one morning to find him gone. He hadn't phoned her until that evening, when he mumbled something about being up north on a kind of pilgrimage to places he'd visited with his mum, and later, Joe. Laying old ghosts to rest and, though he admitted it was crazy, even daring to hope some other relative might appear out of the blue as Joe had done. Wasn't she enough for him? Three days later with no further contact, Elin was beginning to wonder if he'd disappeared for good when Steve came looking for his erratic business partner. Sunny Days was soon forgotten as he offered her sympathy, comfort…and more. She'd succumbed. Once. It only made her realise how much Bede meant to her.

'It was a mistake, Steve, a moment of weakness, and telling him about it wouldn't have done anyone any good. I take it you never said anything either.'

'What do you think?' He gave a hollow laugh. 'Maybe I should go. I could give him a ring tomorrow, or—'

'Don't be daft. Wait here, as long as you don't mind watching me finish this. Though Bede's likely to be late. You staying nearby?'

'Well… I…' This time she refused to fill his silence without prompting. 'It got later than I realised. I was intending to get home. Bit late now, though.'

Elin continued to wait, feeling slightly mean.

'Could I…? I don't suppose…?' He looked away, defeated. 'Well, I've slept in the van before now.'

She relented. 'I'll make up the spare bed later.'

His look of relief was a picture as he picked up his glass. His mischievous eyes turned serious. 'He's going to be late, you said?'

Elin returned his gaze. 'Probably.' He continued to hold her eyes. 'No, Steve.' She began to resume her basketwork, then paused. 'I could make some excuse about wanting to get this finished. About not knowing when he'll be back. But actually, just no.' He gave the slightest nod. 'I regretted it then and there's no way now that—'

He held a hand up. 'It's OK, Elin. That's not why I came, believe me. But, you know…'

'Ever the opportunist.'

'It's what makes me a successful businessman.'

'Are you? We haven't heard from you for a while.'

'You know how it's been.'

She raised her eyebrows.

'I'm rushed off my feet at the moment. I've been working with someone else – sorry Elin, but, you know… Anyway he's gone to pastures new and I don't mind admitting he was never a patch on Bede. Knowledge, problem-solving…' He gave her a crooked smile. 'Who needs a calm, cheerful temperament in a co-worker anyway? So, I've got the possibility of this new hydro contract and there's no way I could do it on my own. You could say it's Bede's specialist subject – do you think he'd be interested in working together again?'

'Who knows? I never did drag out of him what you two argued about.'

Steve looked away, picked up a withy and flicked it idly between his fingers.

'Nothing in particular. He was bloody impossible since…the flood.'

'Since Joe drowned.'

'Yeah.' He sighed. 'Let me down on several occasions – which I admit was unlike him. When he did turn up, he spent most of the time biting my head off about trivia. Don't worry, most of it was before…you know.'

'I know his moods were enough to try the patience of a saint – and you're no saint,' she said. 'I'm sure we can patch things up. He's thought more than once about ringing you.'

'He should have. Like I said, this hydro scheme in Wales – I had a quick look today and I'll be going back tomorrow. I'd love Bede's opinion before I quote, and then his help with the job if I get it. Sorry it's short notice, but…'

Elin smiled, wondering how Steve ever managed to get anything done with his chaotic ways. They passed the time catching up with their news and laughing at his internet dating anecdotes. Eventually, she heard the door.

Bede shed his dripping coat, looking warily from one to the other.

'Well, well. Mr Day.'

Steve grinned. 'Hiya, mate. I've come with a proposition for you. Get yourself settled and I'll tell you about it.'

Bede relaxed, shook his hand and gave him a clap on the back as if they'd parted the best of friends, before giving Elin a hug and a kiss. He looked at the basket she'd managed to complete, noticed the beer bottles and empty glasses, and went to fetch refills plus one for himself.

'So, how was the Horseshoes?' she asked.

'Fine. Big excitement earlier.'

'You won?'

'We did, but that came later. Nope, beginning of the evening. Philip Northcote's got a new car – Bentley, I think. Something like that.'

She knew he'd have taken in every detail, down to the model and the year. 'Go on.'

'They were flocking round it like dogs to a lamp post.' He looked at each of them in turn. 'Honestly, I don't need to say more, do I? When's the world going to *grow up*?'

Steve shrugged. 'Guess you've got to let them have their fun.'

'Fun? How far do things have to go before people realise?' Bede tapped his fingers in agitation against the bottle in his hand. 'Well, no point preaching to the converted. What brings Sunny Days to Alderleat?'

Steve told him about the project he was quoting for.

'OK. I'll come and have a look with you tomorrow.' Bede ran a hand through his hair, picked up a towel and began to rub at the wet ends. 'Whether I can commit to working away for any length of time is another matter.'

'You're not serious,' Elin said. 'Of course you've got to—'

'We can talk about it, love. Let's see if he gets the contract first.'

Living in the real world

It was getting light – grey merging to a paler shade of grey – when Elin watched the Sunny Days van disappear down the lane. Small bubbles in the puddles settled, melting into the ever-changing raindrop circles on the surface of the water, and it seemed as though the only sun she'd seen for days was on the side of Steve's van.

She turned and went in, casting an eye over the basket and noticing slight imperfections she knew no one else ever would, before moving it aside. She began to clear away and wash up the breakfast things.

Kip padded over and lay at her feet, then stirred and sat up as she became aware of tyres crunching on the gravel of the yard. The stuff of men's dreams, Bede's nightmares, glided in. Only a car like that could actually glide over their yard. She tried to maintain her vision of their ancient estate car as homely and practical rather than scruffy, as the Bentley pulled up alongside it.

She turned from the window to put some plates away. Although she was expecting it, the force of Philip Northcote's hammering on the door made her jump.

Dressed immaculately in grey suit and polka-dot tie, he looked imposing even with his waxed jacket draped over his shoulders against the rain. His eyes were blazing fit to evaporate the drops around him.

'Morning, Philip,' she said calmly. Years of living with Bede had made her immune to blazing eyes. 'What can I—'

'Bede in?'

'Sorry, he's just left. Can I help?'

He tutted. 'Might have known. Couldn't stay and face the music. It's about time your husband grew up and started living in the real world.'

How far apart could their definitions of *grown up* and *the real world* possibly be?

'You'd better come in and tell me what this is about.'

He shook his head curtly. 'Isn't it fucking obvious? See that?'

She looked at the gleaming Bentley, raindrops only enhancing the subtle glow of the paintwork, a condescending presence outside their house as though even the car didn't want to be there.

'I see it. And?'

'How can you be so bloody brazen? As if the pair of you haven't been having a good laugh at my expense. Well I hope you can still smile when you get the bill.'

Then she noticed. Two deep parallel scratches scored down the side. A mixture of apprehension and indignation rose inside her. She glared at him.

'Look, if you think Bede would do something like that—'

'I don't *think*.'

How dare he? She folded her arms. 'See him do it, did you?'

'Didn't need to. It's obvious, isn't it?'

'Anything but. He was in a busy pub working and playing pool all evening.'

'After letting me know in no uncertain terms what he thought of me and my car.'

'Just words, Philip.'

He was shaking his head again. 'I suppose this is meant to be some kind of protest for the planet. But there'll be more of your precious resources used up in repairing it. And I'll be sending you the bill.'

'So you said. Feel free to send what you like.' Elin dug her fingernails into her palms; losing her temper wouldn't achieve anything. 'Unless you can prove it was him, there isn't a cat in hell's chance of us paying it.'

'I thought you protesters liked to claim "responsibility" for your irresponsible actions. I'll have the police round.'

'They'll find nothing because there's nothing *to* find.' She looked him in the eye. 'Like last time.'

He stared back. 'So if it wasn't him, who else could it have been?'

Was he actually accusing her? She wouldn't lower herself to deny it. 'I have no idea, sorry.'

'You will be.'

He left.

Elin forced herself to close the door gently – slamming it would achieve nothing – and turned back into the kitchen. She stood for a moment, breathing away her anger. Kip was watching, hackles slightly raised but silent.

'Fat lot of help you were,' she said as she ruffled his ears.

Turning back to the draining board, she picked up Bede's favourite mug to dry it, stowed it in its place on the shelf and stood for a moment staring at it.

The rain had cleared and, before starting on her jobs, Elin went out to walk off her frustration. The dusty, sepia-tinged scent of the May blossom hung on the air, taunting her as she pulled her jacket tighter against the fresh breeze. *Ne'er cast a clout till May is out* – it was hard to remember the false early spring and the week of sunshine they'd enjoyed in April when Fran and Jeff were there. It was as though they'd taken the good weather home with them. Well, they'd had it for a month now – time to give it back. Except she knew it had been as wet in Manchester as in Foxover.

The hawthorn didn't seem to mind. The white sprays arching from the hedgerows and single bushes dotting the hillside created a photo in negative of the landscape, and the scent came in waves as she followed the path that wound its way over the hillside.

The lone bushes looked like abandoned brides, forlorn. An occasional breeze moved their trailing lace-trimmed fingers in a dance to attract their men back. She smiled as she recalled the day she and Bede had first conjured the image, taking it in turns to add details. One night they'd slip down to the river and drown themselves in a tragic ritual on realising their errant husbands-to-be would never return. When they'd planted the willows, he said they provided a safety net, keeping the beautiful hawthorn brides in their place until the summer returned and persuaded them they didn't need husbands to make their lives complete. The only reminder of what might have been were the berries like an annual display of blood-red tears. He hadn't mentioned his mum, but the errant husbands had been his idea.

Kip was running rings around her, following scents, sniffing out burrows. As the path led into Holtwood, the dog gave a small bark, looking back at her, tail waving a beacon. Shaking off the feeling of being a trespasser in a place she had once found reassuring, she followed him into the trees, heading towards the river. She was stopped short by an angry yellow sign glaring at her like a searchlight. Private Land. Keep Out. And another: Danger. Shooting in Progress.

She felt in her inside pocket and drew out a couple of the crumpled flyers and a small tin of drawing pins she carried for such opportunities. The flyers were impossible to smooth fully, but it was the principle; they'd be gone in no time anyway. She tacked *Frack-Free Foxover* over the harsh yellow warnings – it had become habit although she knew it would achieve little more than to make her feel better – then started down the path. Despite the sharp yet homely smell of the wild garlic, and the small carpets of bluebells pooling to either side, the sound of the wind stirring the leaves blended with the birdsong and nearby rushing of the river to play on her nerves like a tense film soundtrack punctuated by the distinctive *chak* of the captive pheasants.

Kip vanished from view. She heard a girl's voice, annoyed at first, then soothing, playful. Crossing the track, which seemed more rutted every time she came, she followed the path to one of her favourite places, a hollow in the land by the river, where the arms and fingers of alders and willows spread in welcome to the clearing they formed. She saw Tamsin there, fussing the dog.

'Hello.' Elin smiled. 'I haven't seen you here before.'

'Oh, I used to come here a lot. We loved playing in the woods when we were little. I realised recently I hadn't been for ages. Needed some peace and quiet. I'm in the middle of revision. Exams coming up, you know?'

She picked up the stick Kip had dropped in front of her and threw it, badly. It splashed into the shallows. Elin watched the dog leap in after it, shuddering as she imagined the shower to come. A dark hollow in the undergrowth on the far bank caught her eye.

'Did you know there are water voles over there, on the opposite bank?'

Tamsin smiled. 'Yeah. I was kind of looking out for them. They're shy, though. I've seen the burrows but no sign of the little beggars.'

Kip came bounding out of the water and shook himself.

'Ratty's certainly not going to show himself while you're around,' Elin said, grabbing the stick and throwing it behind them into the undergrowth. 'I'm glad to see the voles are still there, even with all the disturbance on this side of the river. It'll be a sad day if they go. This place has special memories for us. Bede showed me the burrows and we came here to watch for the water voles the first time he brought me to Foxover.' She smiled. 'Joe told me to make the most of it – said it was as close to romance as Bede was likely to get.'

'That's incredible!' Tamsin was staring into the water.

'Really?' Surely it wasn't that surprising.

'Oh, I mean...that would've been before the floods, yeah?' Elin nodded. 'I meant I'm surprised they came back to the same place after the waters went down.'

She heard evasiveness in Tamsin's voice, but her expression gave nothing away.

'Maybe they're less disturbed by flooding than we are,' Elin said.

'Too right. Mum's still fussing about the damage it did to the gardens and the ground floor of the house. Twice now. The first one seemed the kiss of death for the B&B. She and Dad had blazing rows about what a mistake it was coming here, blaming each other. As if they could've known. But, well, they were already at each other's throats all the time anyway. I mean, it's not as if we get floods every year is it? Both times I just thought it was, like, fun – a good excuse not to go to school.' She stopped suddenly, glanced at Elin. 'Oh, I'm sorry... Until we heard...'

'It's OK.'

'It must have been horrible, losing his dad like that.'

Kip nudged Elin. She took the stick from his mouth and

threw it again. 'Joe was Bede's uncle. He never knew his dad.'

'Oh, that's sad. I mean, I have my moments with my dad, and he was a complete bastard over the divorce, but… How did he die?'

'He doesn't know if he's dead. Literally never knew him. His mother refused to tell him who he was, even when she was dying.' She stopped abruptly and stared across the rippled surface of the water. The river carried her words away and she wished it would turn and flow upstream, taking them back and making them unsaid. 'Anyway, he didn't get on with his stepfather and Joe took the place of his father. Listen, Bede would kill me if he knew I'd told you a word of it.'

Kip had settled at her feet and she stroked him as if to entreat him to silence, too.

'You haven't said anything wrong,' Tamsin said. 'I can sympathise; I'm the only one in my crowd with divorced parents. Don't worry, I won't say a thing.' Her hand drew an invisible zip across her mouth. 'Tell you the truth, it makes him seem more approachable, you know? I'm still not sure what to make of him.'

She looked away, her turn to silently confide to the river that she'd said too much.

'He's better for getting to know, I'll grant you that.' Elin laughed. 'Funny expression, that. Isn't everyone?'

'Not in my experience. I've not exactly been warming to Philip, have I?'

Elin raised her eyebrows. 'And how have you been getting to know him?'

Tamsin pulled a face. 'Our place has been invaded since Mum took up with him.'

So their suspicions had been well founded.

'Honestly, it's doing my head in. I mean, I spend most of my time in my room, but I don't want to, like, have to, you know? Trying to avoid him – can't be doing with the sleazeball, but he's just, like, there. Mum insists I have dinner with them and when he's not ignoring me and blathering on to her, he's trying to get round me.' She mimed vomiting.

Elin could sympathise. She wondered what Kate could possibly see in Philip, but reminded herself of others' opinions of Bede. There was no comparison, but then she wasn't Kate.

'Do you know anything about the car incident?'

'Not the beloved Bentley?' Tamsin wrinkled her nose. 'Picked me up from the bus in it yesterday, like I'm supposed to be impressed. Waving at everyone as we passed through the village like he's lord of the manor. Toad of Toad bloody Hall more like. Embarrassing or what?'

'You didn't hear about the Cowardly Act of Vandalism, then?'

'Ooh, I'm all ears.'

Elin told her all about that morning's visit. Tamsin snorted.

'Genius. Wish I'd thought of it myself.'

'That's more or less what Bede said when I phoned to tell him just now.'

'So it wasn't him?'

'Tamsin!' Elin could swear she looked genuinely disappointed. 'Actually, he'd have been way more sophisticated. The Engineer, they used to call him.'

Tamsin grinned. 'Who did?'

'My friend Fran – you've met her – and I were involved with a group of environmental activists when we were students. At a place called Calsthorpe Wood – not unlike

Holtwood, really, but it was threatened by a road development rather than fracking. It's where Bede and I met – Joe got involved in the protest camp and brought him along. Bede came up with some ingenious ideas for lock-down devices—'

'What?'

'You know, when protestors lock themselves into something heavy and immovable in front of whatever they're trying to protect, so it takes the powers-that-be ages to free them safely.'

'Like chaining yourself to stuff? Wow. Did you ever do any of that?'

'A couple of times. It wasn't pleasant – horribly uncomfortable and it ended in getting arrested – but we just felt we had to do *something*.'

'You got arrested?'

'It never came to too much, thanks to the support and intervention of the activist community. Anyway, it got to the stage where non-violent direct action looked like it was getting us nowhere, so they got Bede to break into the compounds under cover of darkness and use his mechanical skills to slow things down. A delivery truck here, a digger there… Always in a way that no one would get hurt, you understand. He said there was no way you'd catch him lying down in front of one or chaining himself to it, so that was his contribution. He was a reluctant protester at best – said he couldn't really see that it achieved anything – but they'd dangle the opportunity to tinker with an engine in front of him as bait.'

Tamsin laughed. 'I get how a scratch in the paintwork would be well beneath him. Surely it's the best argument you've got to get Philip off his trail.'

'No way. His actions weren't exactly legal, right?' Elin

stood up, brushed herself off and called to Kip. 'Listen, I ought to be getting back. Got tons to do. Do you fancy coming, giving me a hand for a while?'

'Yeah, that'd be great.'

'I've been meaning to ring you – we'd love you to help out. It'd only be pocket money and I'm not sure how often. But Bede's checking out a job today with the guy he used to work with. If that comes off we can definitely make it regular.'

They walked towards the rutted track through the woods and began to pick their way between puddles that gleamed blankly up at them – slow going as Tamsin was determined to preserve her trainers the best she could. They were about to turn off onto the footpath Elin had come by when they heard the crunch and splash of an approaching vehicle. She paused to call Kip to heel as a jeep rounded the corner. The window swished down. Elin glimpsed Silvan in the passenger seat before turning her attention to Philip's mask of disapproval.

'You again.'

'Philip,' she replied curtly.

'This is private land.'

'We're aware of that. We're not doing any harm.' She took a few steps to one side. 'And *this* is a public footpath.'

Tamsin looked at her in admiration and moved to join her, looking defiantly past Philip at Silvan as she did so.

'Not for much longer. I'm applying to have it diverted.'

'You can't do that!'

Philip fixed Elin with a stare. 'If I didn't have cause to be concerned about vandalism, I wouldn't have to take security measures, would I?'

'You can't silence people by diverting a footpath,' Elin said. Silvan gave her a thumbs-up behind Philip's back.

'I'm not doing it to silence anyone,' Philip said. 'Tamsin, do you want a lift home?'

'I'm good.'

He rolled his eyes and reminded her about her exam revision, before revving the engine and turning back to Elin. 'I see you still haven't removed your junk. I won't ask again.'

Elin turned and moved quickly up the path out of range of the mud he was bound to spatter them with as he set off.

'Threat received loud and clear, sir,' she muttered to Tamsin as she caught up and they headed through the woods before striking out across the hillside. The fields below and to the side were still clear of anything but a couple of surveying poles; she wondered for how long. 'If we want him to leave us anything to retrieve, that's our first job.'

'Does that mean we can make a raft? I've seen you at it a couple of times before. Always thought it'd be fun to join in.'

'You should've come and asked. Not today, though. I never thought I'd say it, but I don't want to spend any longer in those woods than I have to.' She swallowed her rising anger. 'Time to give the tractor an outing. You ever seen an electric tractor?'

'You what?'

'Our pride and joy. Well, Bede's baby, really – he converted it. He's planning to disembowel the car next.'

'You're joking.'

Elin smiled. 'He threatened to, but I've put my foot down and told him we'll have to recycle a write-off.'

'The beloved Bentley mysteriously dies at the Engineer's hands…'

'Don't tempt him.'

'How come you haven't got an electric car already?'

'There's no way we could afford one new, and there's hardly a thriving second-hand market yet. When we first had the idea of converting an EV, Bede and Joe decided we probably do more miles on the land than going places, so the tractor came first. It was probably more straightforward for him to learn on, too.' She smiled. 'They were about to start looking for a suitable victim – um, I mean car to convert – when Joe died.'

She glanced at Tamsin, telling herself she'd given away so many personal confidences already that another little detail wouldn't harm. 'It's one of those things Bede...hasn't been able to face since then.'

Tamsin nodded, apparently accepting it all as perfectly reasonable.

Back at Alderleat, she disappeared upstairs to change into some borrowed old clothes – she was reluctant to go home in case Kate had other plans for her – while Elin busied herself hitching the trailer to the tractor. She was surprised she still noticed how the tyre noise and rattling of the hitching gear was louder than the barely audible electric motor. The between-showers sun glinted off the body Bede had sprayed a glorious purple, her favourite colour and a bid to prove it wasn't all mundane functionality. The bodywork in turn was usually outshone by his glow of pride, which had hardly faded since he'd first driven it out. Despite initial scepticism, including Joe's, the electric workhorse had served them well for a couple of years now, powered without guilt by electricity from their turbine. The heavy battery on the back even increased the traction. He liked to pronounce that it was far more meaningful than some protest that was unlikely to make the powers-that-be even pause for breath.

Tamsin came out of the house, Kip at her heels, and Elin felt sorry Bede wasn't there to see her look of admiration. She clambered into the cab, looking as though she was going to enjoy working here as much as Elin was having her around.

An idealist with a vision

Bede looked up at the turbine. He ran his hand over the texture of the wood, recalling hours perfecting the delicate scaffold. It wasn't particularly tall; he thought about the white giants taking possession of hilltops and how they wanted to do it differently. This beauty, carefully situated to catch the prevailing wind, was enough for what they needed. He checked the safety harness yet again, then, trying to remember climbing trees as a boy to suppress the nerves he always felt, began to climb.

At the top he extended the platform, checked it was firmly locked in place and clipped the safety harness to the bracket. This fine day with just a hint of a breeze had come at the perfect time for him to service it before starting the job with Steve. They were quietly confident they'd get the contract and he looked forward to reviving their Sunny Days partnership. Looking back, it was hard to trace how after years of friendly banter, Steve had suddenly snapped.

Perhaps because when you were wallowing in self-pity and taking it out on everyone else wasn't the best moment to bang on about how Sunny Days might be better than nursing internal combustion engines at the garage in Halbury but you still weren't going to solve the climate crisis without more radical change.

If you can't say anything positive… Bede barely batted an eyelid as he shrugged Joe's nagging away. He *had* always felt that what they were doing was significant, and had tried to keep his growing cynicism light. Obviously not light enough, he had to acknowledge. He'd been stunned last autumn when they'd driven home from a job under a cloud and Steve hadn't been back in touch. But over the last few days, they'd worked together on the hydro scheme assessment with renewed companionship, and it felt good.

He spread his arms, face raised to the light breeze, and momentarily lost himself to the elation of the height, the house and buildings below, the river winding its steady way through the expansive landscape. Their world. A movement on the road caught his eye. He watched Philip's flash car pull into Kate's drive and fought down a surge of anger. Maybe it was a good thing he'd been out when the bastard had called and laid into Elin. Maybe he'd have really given him something to complain about. Why did the brash idiot have to keep provoking him?

Forcing calm on himself, he put on his glasses and opened the side of the turbine, ready to concentrate on what he was here for: checking, cleaning, lubricating. He noticed someone walking along the footpath that crossed their land. Fearing the prospect of an interruption, he told himself, childlike, that if he didn't acknowledge the approaching figure, they weren't in the same world. They would simply walk on.

'Hey, Bede!'

He muttered Silvan's name by way of greeting and grudgingly paused in his tinkering. Walk on, don't stop, just walk on.

Silvan stopped and looked up, a hand shielding his spiky-haired brow against the bright sky. 'Is something wrong up there?'

'Just servicing it.'

He took a step closer. 'Mind if I—?'

'I do mind, yes. Need to concentrate.'

He turned away, his fingers involuntarily checking the safety harness carabiner, each slight movement seeming to make the structure sway although he knew it was perfectly sound. He didn't have to look to know he was still being watched. He took a deep breath, willed Silvan to go, and tried to think about the job in hand.

'That looks really—'

'Please.' He barked it out like a teacher to a disobedient child. He had no desire to talk, to explain, to be a show. 'Elin's in the house if you want something.'

Turning deliberately to concentrate on his work, he tried not to let irritation snare him into carelessness.

'All right, all right, I can tell when I'm not wanted. See you later.'

He paused long enough to make Bede feel guilty before trudging on down the hill. Why should he feel guilty about wanting to be left alone?

A little later, he headed back towards the house, replete with the satisfaction of a job well done. As he passed the fire pit, he paused a moment to gaze out at the river, lifeblood of the land. The water was higher than usual for this time of year, but the greenness of the spring fields beneath the peacefully drifting clouds gave the gleaming ribbon a promising air of fertility, its concealed threat distant.

Elin had suggested more than once that this would be a perfect location for a hut or a yurt, somewhere they could offer as a holiday let – make a little money, even have people to stay and help on the smallholding. Joe had been keen, too. Bede had always managed to deflect it while not refusing outright. He wanted to like the idea, but the reality of it made him feel invaded.

She'd even suggested it needn't be permanent in her attempts to persuade him.

Can't you at least give it a try?

An uneasy guilt crept up on him. His failure to share her enthusiasm wasn't exactly outright dismissal, but it was another aspect of their lives where she quietly let him have his way. He'd never even learned Welsh well enough to hold a fluent conversation with her in her first language. And looking back over the last two years, he was aware how close he'd come on several occasions to pushing her away. Yet she'd stuck with him, and he'd vowed more than once to make a better job of letting her know how much she meant to him. He had an uneasy feeling that on their recent holiday exploring north Wales she'd been giving him a last chance, and he was relieved they'd finally turned the corner. It occurred to him now that the escape to the country they could provide for others might be a mobile one, offering Elin and himself the chance to escape more often. He wasn't insensitive enough to think that this was as important as some of the other issues that hovered between them, but it would be a gesture.

By the time he reached the yard, he was smiling to himself as he looked forward to telling her of his change of heart. A soft, intermittent murmur of voices drifted out through the open window together with a hint of the rich fragrance of brewing. Elin listening to the radio as she worked was part of the soundscape of home, and he liked the way the hoppy scent of natural creativity warmed the house.

After a few moments in the switch-room checking and reconnecting the system, he stepped outside to watch the turbine blades beginning to turn majestically. The movement was only slight because of the calm day he'd chosen for the work, but it was there, ready to continue ensuring their independence. He increasingly believed that his main defence against a world whose ways he resented was to distance himself from it. Elin still dreamed of changing the world.

Back at the house, he realised one of the voices floating through the window was hers. Not the radio, then. He heard her laugh and tucked the holiday home away behind the defensive wall the second voice conjured. Walking in, he savoured the smell of hops as he would a glass of the beer it would become. Elin was in the utility room, putting the beer to bed ready for fermentation in the large vessel they'd rigged up together. Silvan was leaning against the wall, watching and idly fondling Kip's ears. Honestly, that soft dog would suck up to anyone.

'Hi, Bede,' Elin said into the kind of silence that hinted they'd just been talking about him. 'All sorted?'

'Fine.' He nodded at Silvan and forced a smile before going over to the sink to wash his hands. 'Running like a dream. How's the ale coming on?'

'It's going to be a good one.' She chatted about the new hops she was using and adjustments she'd made to the recipe as they followed him into the kitchen. 'There's tea in the pot, but it could be a bit stewed.'

'Don't worry; the stronger the better.' He sat at the table, placing his mug to form a neat triangle with the two already there, and enjoyed the welcome weight of Kip flopping at his feet beneath the table.

Bede looked at Silvan. 'You have my undivided attention now. What can I tell you?'

Elin flashed him a look. His words had come out more harshly than he intended.

'You what?' Silvan frowned.

'You were interested in how the turbine works. I was preoccupied.' He caught Elin's eye again. 'Sorry if I was a bit…short with you.'

'Oh, it doesn't matter.' He waved a hand, whether to accept the apology or dismiss any sign of interest, Bede couldn't tell. 'I just fancied joining you and having a look. I don't know much about mechanical stuff but it looked fun up there.'

'Fun.' Bede raised his eyebrows. 'Sod principles and common sense – savings on fuel bills, even. Maybe we've been going wrong all these years – we should be switching people on to clean energy by emphasising the *fun* side of things.'

'Nice one.' Silvan grinned. He put on a TV presenter's voice. 'Why not give the kids a novel climbing frame and power your house at the same time?'

Bede smiled uncertainly and sensed Elin relax slightly.

'I'll start thinking of some designs,' he said. 'Could be on to a winner.'

He drank a mouthful of tea and pulled a face.

'Shall I make some more?' Elin said.

'I'm fine, thanks.' Bede turned back to Silvan. 'So, how's life on the Northcote estate, grooming pheasants and the like?'

'You don't honestly think—'

Bede laughed. 'I don't mean their magnificent plumage. The sordid kind. Readying them for the satisfaction of men's dark desires.'

'If it's a way of venting those dark desires so they don't get unleashed elsewhere, that can't be bad. Anyway, it's only temporary and I'm learning a lot. I bet you didn't pick up all your skills on that idealistic commune of yours.'

'True.' Bede frowned at Elin. Had she really told him about Calsthorpe Wood? It had been years ago, but certain aspects still rankled and they rarely talked about it themselves, let alone to others. 'Just make sure you use what you learn for the right things.'

'Oh, I intend to.' Silvan leaned forward with an air of mystery. 'I could be useful to you. With Northcote. Eyes and ears – give you early warning of his intentions.'

Bede frowned. 'Why would you do that?'

'I like you two and it pisses me off the way he singles you out. I know you have your disagreements, especially with the drilling proposals, but there are plenty of others involved in the objections. Why you? I don't believe you had anything to do with vandalising his property, either time, so why's he got it in for you?'

Elin glanced at Bede and he widened his eyes in a silent warning. 'Apart from the obvious,' she said, 'Bede's uncle Joe was friendly with Philip's mother, Marjorie – do you know her?'

'Haven't met her yet.'

'She offered Joe this place and—'

'Then we came along,' Bede intervened, 'and before you know it, there's a turbine blotting the skyline, a mill stream cutting across the land and the riverbank's littered with a short-rotation coppice plantation that's "not the way we've always done things". Who'd have thought it? Native willows on floodplain land that's not much use for anything else, helping to anchor the soil and keep flooding in check.' He rolled his eyes. 'Disgusting. Northcote was at the forefront of every objection to what we've done, before he even came back to live here.'

Silvan nodded. 'Yeah, I've heard him on that subject. You know – any objections he made were through the proper channels, and he's accepted the result. You lot, on the other hand—'

'There's no comparison!' Elin said. 'You can't honestly—'

'Hey, hey. Don't shoot the messenger. I know where you're coming from. Though when I came here, heard about his plans, I was swayed at first. He's a decent enough bloke; he can be persuasive. Apart from the locals' hysteria over the dangers—' Both Bede and Elin were about to speak but he cut them off. 'His words, not mine. The risk is tiny, he says – even non-existent, given proper test drilling – and local communities will be well compensated out of the profits.'

'Bribery!' Bede interrupted. 'He'll have a job on if he thinks he can buy Foxover.'

Silvan laughed. 'I'm sure they're not all idealists like you. Offer them enough… I bet even you have your price. Anyway, apart from all that, he reckons it's cleaner than coal, way better than importing gas. A perfect opportunity to tide us over in the short-to-medium term.'

'Medium term? Scientists have given us twelve years to get our act together if we want to avoid—'

'Oh, he's got an answer for that one too. Nothing to date has deteriorated anywhere near as quickly as the doom-mongers said it would.'

'Doom-mongers?' Bede thumped the table. 'It's happening as we speak! Do you, Northcote and your kind want to make a rational decision about how we move into the future, or wait till things finally go so wrong you bloody *have* to do something about it and it's too late anyway?'

'Don't lump me in with him.' Silvan remained irritatingly calm. 'I'm just saying what you're up against.'

'We know what we're up against.'

'Yeah, sorry. Anyway, I've been thinking about it a lot. Reading all that stuff on the Frack-Free Foxover website. I must admit, at first I wanted to just, you know, have a laugh at the nimbys and the hippies. But it made a lot of sense.

I'm impressed – you know your stuff.' He looked at Bede with open admiration.

'I've done my share of research,' he said, 'but Elin's the one studied environmental science. She put most of it together.'

'Kudos.' Silvan grinned at her. 'Anyway, like I said, I want to help.'

'So come to our meetings,' she said. 'Write to the planners. There's still time.'

'I can't do either of those. I'd lose my job.'

'Can't understand why the fuck you want to work for him.' Bede picked up his almost-cold tea and forced down a gulp, wishing he hadn't refused Elin's offer of a fresh brew. She gave him another stern look.

'Everyone's entitled to change their mind,' Silvan said. 'I'm looking round, but in the meantime I've got a living to make. I can do my bit, you know, in other ways.'

'Let us know if you hear anything useful, then.' Bede exchanged a look with Elin. He seriously doubted Silvan could do much, but had no desire to burst the bubble of a new convert.

The beer was just coming to life, tiny flocks of yeast and impurities beginning to rise to the surface as the fermentation process began. Elin breathed in the scent, thick enough to be a taste, as she heard Bede come in. It had been a busy hour; Tamsin had arrived on her way home from the school bus just after Silvan left. Elin smiled as she recalled how the timing and the girl's flushed cheeks suggested they'd crossed paths. She had no sooner arrived than Frank Barnham had appeared at the door, telling Bede breathlessly some sheep had got onto their land. The three of them had gone out to help round them up and patch up the fence, and they'd offered to help with more permanent repairs the next day.

'That's got rid of that lot,' Bede said as he brought a waft of cool evening air through the door. Kip wagged his way over to remind him it was teatime and it had better be a good one to make up for taking second place to a bunch of loose sheep. 'There's something I've been wanting to talk to you about.'

'What Silvan was saying?'

'Way more important than that.' She flashed him a look of reproach but noticed the mischief in his eyes before rising to it. 'More…personal, anyway. Do you fancy a bonfire after dinner?'

'Sounds good,' she said. 'Might as well make the most of a gap in the showers.'

'Gap? This is the onset of summer.' Bede spread his arms. 'Prepare for drought!'

Along with beer bottles and glasses, they took the tarp and strung up a shelter against the curtain of rain that hung over the far side of the vale. Even if it didn't come any closer it cast a shadow over the sunset, but she didn't care as she laid and lit a fire in their stone fire-pit. Bede handed her a glass of beer. He took her hand, looked at the dust from the firelighting in the tiny wrinkles that mirrored the ingrained dirt contouring his own fingers, and talked about their day's work as if they were the only people to grow their own food and brew their own beer, to harness the power of the sun, wind and water in defiance of a resource-hungry society. Just as she knew she was the first, the only woman he had ever loved.

'So. What was it you wanted to talk to me about?' she

asked as she snuggled up to him and he put his arm round her.

'Remember your idea of a holiday place here?' he asked.

'You mean the project you weren't interested in because you're, quote, "an engineer, not a builder"?'

'Do you store up all my nuggets of negativity like that?'

He gazed out at the view over the rim of his glass. She felt slightly guilty.

'Of course I don't.' He shook his head slightly and she continued talking to the silence. 'I remember thinking, actually, you're an idealist with a vision that's worth sharing with visitors. I'd still love to give it a go. Bring in some more income, have a few more people around.'

'Well, I've decided I agree with you.'

He surprised her by talking animatedly, hands sketching the air, about finding an old caravan – something they could tow away themselves, too, whenever they needed to get away – and breathing new life into it. He seemed to mean it.

'What's brought this on?'

'I…I've been feeling bad about rejecting your idea. It was silly of me. It's a good one.'

He kissed her. She brushed a wind-blown strand of hair from his face, letting her hand linger on his cheek. They drew apart and raised their glasses to the future.

'But then again,' Elin said, 'it could all turn out to be pointless if that bastard's going to ravage the land and pollute the water. If we're going to have our lives taken over campaigning against it.' She sighed and gazed over towards Holtwood, unable to believe it could possibly happen. 'What did you make of the way Silvan was talking?'

'Sounds like he's beginning to regret who he's working for.'

'Philip Northcote?'

'Who else?'

'He could be here to keep an eye on us. Infiltrating.'

Bede sat up, drawing away slightly. 'You do come out with some stuff sometimes, love. Foxover's hardly a hotbed of anti-establishment dissent.'

She cuffed him playfully. 'You're so easy to wind up. But you never know. Remember Kelly at Calsthorpe? The one whose boyfriend vanished without trace and everyone was convinced he was a spy? It happens.' She was beginning to enjoy herself. 'Or it could be the other way round – Silvan working for a protest group, against Northcote.'

'Nice idea, but that'd mean he's on our side – surely he'd have told us.' He turned serious. 'Listen, El, he's simply going to try and sneak into the Grange office and find out more about the plans. Just a young bloke adding a bit of drama to his life.'

Elin turned to look at him, his sharp profile softened by gust-blown wisps of hair. Her joking hid an underlying unease. 'Maybe he can help us with something closer to home. Remember what he said – why us? I can't help wondering whether Northcote's actively trying to discredit us. Framing you deliberately.'

'Framing?' He laughed dismissively. 'He'll have to do better than that. Two trivial misdemeanours – I wouldn't even call them crimes.'

'Whatever. But he's got his hands on Holtwood to one side and his foot in Kate's door on the other. What if he's after Alderleat? If the fracking goes ahead, God forbid, we've got land adjacent to his that would be useful.'

Kip came to settle at Bede's feet and he reached out absently to stroke his coat. 'So why wouldn't he just make us an offer?'

'Because he thinks we conned Marjorie into giving it away for next to nothing, so he'll not be up for offering a market price. Anyway, what price would you sell at?'

'I wouldn't. No way. But bloody hell, love, there must be easier ways of getting people to leave. Are you suggesting he vandalised his own pheasant pens? Keyed his precious car?'

It sounded crazy when he put it like that. 'Just thinking out loud. Even if attempting to drive us out is a bit far-fetched, he could still be trying to distract us, stop us kicking up a fuss. Or to turn people against us, discredit the protest.'

'Those are quite some conspiracy theories. We just take each step as it comes. Listen to anything Silvan says and decide for ourselves if we want to act on it.' He stood abruptly. 'It's happening again. The man and all he represents taking over our lives. It's not what we came out here for.' He picked up his notebook. 'Let's see to our own plans. That holiday home.'

Elin stayed where she was for a moment, watching his familiar stride as he paced the contour, her eye drawn from his purposeful silhouette to the last traces of sunset reddening the horizon.

25th May 2001

I spend most weekends going up to Calsthorpe Wood; it's a great little place they've got going there even though we all know it's only temporary – that road's going to go ahead and then we'll have to face the doom and gloom. Then again, who knows, this might be the time we win, the time the idiots finally see sense.

The average age of the community is about half mine, but it doesn't seem to bother anyone, least of all me – or Sophie, who's the one that counts. I'm way more into the community than the campaigning, but that's fine – my green fingers have proved invaluable (like, they have enough to eat now) and I like turning my hand to most things. I leave the politics to Graham, Sophie and the others. Grey likes to think he's in charge, but it's really Tig, his lady, who's the earth mother everyone loves. There are shifting numbers, anything from a dozen to twenty or so. Fran who I met the first time comes and goes regularly with an ever-changing group from uni. I get on particularly well with Steve who's taken time out to live here more or less permanently. He's an electrician in 'real' life, about as handy as our Bede and not much older so there's a bit of healthy rivalry going on there.

But it's not all roses. (More a case of useful veg and herbs, ha ha.) I guess I'm turning to this diary again in case I get a eureka moment of what to do. I'm a bit worried about our Bede. Oh, he's doing OK for himself. Renting his own little flat and he's doing an apprenticeship as a mechanic at the garage where he hung around most

Saturdays and weekday evenings when he was growing up. Even with no Markhams at home to escape from, he's still never happier than when he's making and doing. The rest of the time he seems to spend taking himself off on long walks, foraging or just being – observing, learning. God knows what the lads at the garage make of him, but he's a good worker and seems well-liked enough from what I've seen.

He goes a bit further afield now he's got the bike. Motorbike, that is. Loves the beast, and now he can take himself off to Calsthorpe Wood even at times I don't. When I first offered to bring him here – I was feeling a bit guilty I hadn't seen him for a few weeks – he didn't seem too thrilled. Said the whole idea of going off by himself was exactly that – to be by himself. Apart from saying he needn't get sarky with me, I convinced him that, like me, they're the sort of people who understand if he wants to be left to his own devices sometimes. He's made himself useful – you'd think a set of anti-road protestors wouldn't appreciate a motor mechanic, but they're kind of pragmatic and they still need to get themselves and their stuff around. And our Bede has a way of looking at a practical problem, something people have been scratching their heads over or 'getting round to' for ages, and just diving in and sorting it out – anything from an engine to an assault course for the kids.

But that's exactly what's worrying me. As the last battle looms – there's an appeal hearing next week but I can't see it going any other way – we're preparing for an onslaught. Calsthorpe Wood will have to go. Grey's determined not to take the king's shilling of compulsory purchase money (which is nothing compared to the spiritual value anyway) until the last possible moment, so we're morally entitled to be here even though we should actually have been gone ages ago. And in the meantime, the whole machinery – literal and figurative – is gathering ready to pounce.

So they've got this notion of creeping into the compounds and disabling their vehicles and equipment. The idea being if they delay the big inward surge to the site for as long as possible, we might be able to grab a few headlines, since if this appeal doesn't work it's the furthest we or anyone can take it in the courts and that'll be curtains. Not sure if the good old British public has got bored or it's a deliberate ploy by the establishment to keep us out of the media, but the wider world has been largely silent on this one and in my humble opinion it's every bit as devastating as any that did make the headlines.

Bede told me about the plan after I arrived this afternoon. Faced with his great puppy-dog enthusiasm, I thought cool idea, but now it's sunk in I'm worried. Injunctions, trespass, alleged breaches of the peace are one thing, but this would be criminal damage. Another thing that he, they, could get put away for. He's 18 for fuck's sake. What a start to adult life that'd be.

This sabotage needs to be done last-minute to rule out the chance of 'them' repairing the damage, so I guess I've still got time to talk him out of it, but my clumsy attempt earlier on turned into our first row.

I suppose he's right that he doesn't have to listen to me, and, shocked though I was to hear it, I also suppose he's right that my main motivation for coming here in the first place was to get between Sophie's organic cotton sheets. But if he thinks that means I'm not committed now, he couldn't be more wrong. I just hate to think they're using him, Grey in particular – making the most *of his skills and abilities, yes and why not, but also getting him to go that bit beyond what anyone would consider reasonable, by playing on the fact he's a couple of years younger than any of them (except Tig's little 'uns) and feels the need to prove himself. And it's not just to Grey and Steve. I've seen the way he's been looking at the Welsh girl, Elin, one of Fran's mates from uni who's appeared on the scene recently.*

Deftly stilled

Iridescent scales flashed in the early morning sunlight. Bede removed the fish from the line and deftly stilled it. He paused for a moment, mesmerised by the leaden eye and gleaming body, thanking it in the silent ritual he'd developed over the years. Although he'd probably have ridiculed himself for the like at any other time, it always felt right, there on the bank, in that special moment of a catch.

His gratitude wasn't only for the sustenance, but for the calm and patience he found when immersed in the hours of watching and waiting by the water's edge. And – he allowed himself to think it – for the deep friendship and love of the man who'd given him his first rod, who'd first sat an unhappy teenager down on the banks of a river and introduced him to the time-honoured joys of angling. He realised how much he'd missed the companionable hours with Joe on the banks of canals and rivers, learning about the different kinds of bait, deciphering the mysteries of rod and line. At first he'd been uncomfortable with the moment of killing, but long before he truly understood the word *hypocrite* he thought it was wrong to like eating fish if you couldn't hack catching it.

He looked with satisfaction at the three trout in the wicker creel Elin had made for him – one each for their dinner that night and one to take to Marjorie – and began to pack up. A flurry of tiny waves on the wind-riffled river caught his eye and he paused, daring to look downstream.

He should have done this long ago. Instead of fearing the river, he should have known the magic of reliving their shared activities wouldn't desert him, should have trusted the water to carry away his grief and anger.

Didn't I tell you?

The now-familiar voice made it all the more ironic that he had Robert Markham to thank for recalling him to the river today. He smiled as he gathered his things together and began to walk up the edge of the field, the light breeze raising soothing whispers from the willows before catching in his hair. Was this a first – gratitude towards his stepfather?

He'd gone into the house from the workshop the evening before to find Elin looking perplexed.

'You'll never guess who phoned. Your dad.'

'What?' The world shifted around him.

'Robert.'

He almost felt relieved. '*Step*dad.'

'Yes, sorry.'

Irritation flowed fast in the wake of relief. 'What the fuck did he want?'

'Bede! I'm not surprised he sounded glad you weren't around. Sam's getting married.' She held up a hand to silence him. 'He was wondering, given the occasion, whether you might…it might be good to see you again. For them to meet me. Bit of a reconciliation.'

Why did she seem to find this so hard? It wasn't her past.

'He must be joking! Did he really…? I hope you told him where they can stick their bloody wedding.'

'I told him I'd talk to you about it. Why not, Bede?'

She'd never really understood.

'You do realise he doesn't actually want us to go? This is just his way of letting me know how pissed off he is that I didn't invite them to ours. Not that he'd have wanted to come, you understand. But God, it must have stuck in his craw to know I had the independence, the freedom, the *autonomy* not to ask.'

He'd refused to pick up the phone and give their apologies. Elin had insisted it was the least he could do. Thrown into turmoil by the intrusion when the two of them had other things to worry about, he'd lain awake until late into the night and woken ridiculously early. And yes, he did actually have Robert Markham to thank, for being the catalyst that finally drove him back to the sanctuary of the river.

Pausing to savour the blush of sunrise above the peaceful riverflow, he wondered why the prospect of a simple 'sorry, we can't make it' had seemed at all daunting. He didn't have to justify himself. He'd tried to get along while his mum was alive, but the Markhams meant nothing to him now. He preferred not to think of them as his past – apart from his mum, the memories that meant something to him were of Joe, of Elin, here at Alderleat. On the paternal side there was nothing, not even a name. Not a void; he preferred to think of it as a blank canvas.

He resumed his walk home: the buildings nestling along the fold of the mill stream and the turbine rising above the trees on its shoulder of land. A blank canvas on which all this was painted.

'You're looking cheerful this morning.'

With a screech of brakes, Tamsin brought her bike to a halt and paused with a foot to the ground, school bag in the basket on the front. He waved, noticing as he did so that both Kate's and Philip's cars were in her driveway. It seemed the bike had been her personal choice, not forced on her by the lack of a lift.

'It'd be hard to be anything else on a morning like this,' he said as he closed the field gate behind him. 'Why don't you bring the bike next time you come round? I'll smooth those brakes for you and check why your chain's been slipping.'

'Thanks.' Frowning, she eyed him with suspicion. 'I didn't know you were into fishing.'

'Oh, I am. This is the first time since Joe died, that's all.'

It felt satisfying. No more euphemisms, no more hiding it away in some murky depth of non-acceptance. 'Since Joe died' – a sad but natural fact of life.

She was still looking at him strangely. 'I'd never have thought you... Oh, I get it – you put them back, yeah?'

He showed her the contents of the creel. Her face fell.

'But you're veggie, you and Elin. Like me.'

Bede waved an arm in a broad arc encompassing the river, the willows and the fields beyond. 'We are, largely. But it's not all about the cruelty and destruction of factory farming. I don't need to tell you that meat eating and livestock rearing is disastrous for the planet in terms of land use and emissions. Localised wild fishing, on the other hand, isn't upsetting any ecosystem. I'd be the first to stop if it did.' Her eyes were still boring into him. 'You think I'm a hypocrite, don't you?'

'It's still taking something else's life.'

'Can't deny it.' He shifted the basket on his shoulder. 'I try to be quick and humane. Prey and predator is...natural, and I only take what we need. There are some questions have no easy answers. Contradictions emerge if you think deeply enough about anything.'

'Sounds like you're just wriggling out of it to me.' Tamsin glanced at her watch. 'Shit, sorry, I can't risk missing the school bus. Got to be off. But I'm not leaving it at that. Don't think you're off the hook.'

'Ha ha.'

She caught his eye and smiled for the first time since she'd noticed his fishing rod and waders.

'I look forward to the debate,' he said, grinning back.

As he watched her cycle down the lane, Philip Northcote's Bentley drew up alongside him. The window swished down.

'I'm glad I've bumped into you.' Philip frowned at the sight of Bede's fishing tackle. 'I hope you're entitled to do that. Bridge Farm leases the fishing rights on this stretch to—'

'The riparian owners' rights along the Alderleat bank stayed with the house. And I have an up-to-date rod licence, not that it's any of your business. Anything else I can help you with?'

Philip picked up an envelope from the passenger seat.

'This is for you.'

Bede raised his eyebrows in a tacit question. Philip said nothing, apparently waiting. It was obvious what it contained but Bede duly opened it and skimmed the contents, tutting and sucking air through his teeth.

'What a rip-off.' He looked up. 'New wing? Two new doors? The guy I used to work for in Halbury's a bodywork wizard. He could've… But I understand. Main dealer, warranties and all that. I sympathise – but I guess it's small change for someone like you.'

He made to hand it back.

'Quite the comedian,' Philip said. 'There's a note with it – I'm giving you seven days. I've just taken a picture with the dashcam as proof of you reading it. Pay up or I'll see you in court.'

'No need to wait seven days,' Bede said, surprised by his own calm. 'As far as I'm concerned you can instigate proceedings now. Except you won't because you know you don't have a leg to stand on. Where was your dashcam when you needed it?' He ripped the bill and letter into several pieces. 'This'll have to go for recycling. You could've e-mailed it. What a waste.'

'Oh, for God's sake.'

His tone never failed to wind Bede up. 'I know I might as well save my breath. You don't give a toss about waste, do you? Just as you don't give a toss about industrialising the landscape, polluting the groundwater or digging up fossil fuels that should be kept in the ground!'

'Oh, please. It's nothing I haven't heard before. I have the interests of this community at heart too, you know – I just have more realistic ideas about how to serve them. I haven't got time to hang around talking in circles with you here and now,' he snatched the remains of the letter Bede was thrusting at him, 'but I suggest you keep your arguments reasoned and make them through the proper channels.'

'Pity we haven't got the financial resources to make sure the "proper channels" are listening.'

Philip's air of pained reasonableness gave way to anger. 'You'd be well advised to keep insinuations like that to yourself.'

He sped off, giving Bede the dubious satisfaction of having touched a nerve. Shouldering his fishing creel, he regretted the intrusion into his new-found calm and once again wished they could simply be left alone to get on with their lives.

The following Saturday, Tamsin knocked at the door bright and early. Well, early at least, Elin thought – yet another dull, showery day could hardly be called bright. She poured her a coffee and laid out bread, jam and honey on the kitchen table.

'How're you getting on with the glamping place?' Tamsin asked as she spread honey thickly on a slice of bread. 'Can't wait to see the developments.'

Elin smiled, wondering what Bede would say if he knew they were preparing to offer 'glamping'. After helping Brian dismantle a shed and reclaiming the timber, they'd spent the last few days erecting a wooden structure on the chassis of a stock trailer that had been slowly decaying at Frank Barnham's. 'We've got a frame up and we're about ready to start on the roof.'

'Wow, quick work. I meant to say, my dad's got a couple of skylights lying around in his garage. I think they're still there and I'm sure he won't be needing them. Would they be any use?'

'Sounds wonderful if you don't mind asking.'

'Provided I can have a go at helping with the building.'

Tamsin had made herself at home in just a couple of weeks. Elin would never have guessed she'd enjoy getting her hands dirty or be so willing to pitch in.

'Sorry to disappoint. I really need you in the greenhouse.' Elin looked at her sternly. 'All day. I've got a shift at the shop this afternoon but that doesn't mean you can let Bede sneak you off to help with the caravan.' She shrugged. 'Maybe some overtime tomorrow? You could have a go then.'

'No can do.' She looked at her warily, chewing a large mouthful of bread and honey.

Elin could imagine the reason. 'Other plans?'

'Yeah.' Even the coffee cup Tamsin raised to her face wasn't enough to conceal her excitement.

'Are you seeing him again?'

'Who?' Tamsin said, avoiding her eyes.

'I'll take that as a yes. Silvan seems quite a character. I'm pleased for you.'

Tamsin relaxed a little. 'He's off seeing his mates in Birmingham today, and a gig tonight. My mate Lauren's coming for a sleepover tonight in any case,' she added as if keen to prove that life went on as usual. 'She's just passed her test, looking forward to having her mum and dad's car for the evening. Then Silvan's taking me out tomorrow. Up into the mountains, or even to the coast, depending on the weather.'

'Is Kate cool with that?'

Tamsin paused, her knife hovering over the bread. She looked at Elin, back at the bread. 'Well… I sort of let her assume I'll be going back with Lauren. I'm sure she won't question it.'

'Don't you think you should tell her the truth? What if anything happens?'

'What d'you mean, "anything happens"?'

Elin backed off a little from all the possibilities. 'Like she finds out you've been lying?'

'If I told her she probably wouldn't let me go.' She looked defiantly at Elin, dropping the knife with a clatter. 'Honestly, Elin, I thought you'd be different. But you're, like, on my case same as everyone else. The minute something good happens… Don't you remember what it's like?' She waved a hand at the ceiling and the creaking floorboards of Bede moving around upstairs. 'With him?'

Elin did remember, and what it was like to be surrounded by people hinting while trying not to say outright that she was doing the wrong thing. Realising she was becoming fond of Tamsin, she nevertheless wondered how she'd managed to land the role of confidante. She sighed. 'Yes, I do. I hope you have a lovely day out. Just…' Just what? 'Take it steady. Watch yourself.'

'Jesus, what d'you think's gonna happen?'

'Nothing, but…he's several years older than you, for a start.'

'Thanks for the words of wisdom. I hadn't noticed. So what's wrong with twenty-four? Are you and Bede exactly the same age?'

Elin shook her head in exasperation. 'He's a year younger than me, actually. And I was in my first year at uni when we met. Not sixteen.'

Tamsin sighed dramatically. 'Like I said, I wouldn't have had you down—'

'Oh, we know where you are, and you've got our number.' Relenting, Elin raised her own eyes towards upstairs and smiled. 'Just don't do anything I wouldn't.'

They both relaxed. There was nothing like a shared old chestnut to smooth things over. Elin gathered the plates and cups and went to the sink.

'Morning, girls. I hope you've left some breakfast for me.'

Bede wandered in. His shower-wet hair straggled in tendrils over his bare shoulders, tiny rivulets watering the garlanded leaves of his tattoo. He turned to put the kettle on, revealing the stylised swirls of the river winding down his back. It was so much a part of him that it took Tamsin staring to make Elin see it anew. He glanced down as if he felt the same way, then reached for a T-shirt from the drying rack in the corner.

'Hold on,' Tamsin said. 'That's amazing, let me get a proper look. Um, hope you don't mind me saying…'

'Thanks. 'Course I don't mind.'

She nodded appreciatively. 'Looks even better in the flesh.'

'What do you mean?'

'You know – I've seen a couple of pics online. Googled that protest you were involved in. The Engineer.' She glanced at Elin, who sighed inwardly. 'You haven't changed much.'

Bede pulled the T-shirt over his head, turned and busied himself with the coffee. His irritation was tangible. 'Where d'you hear about that?'

'I was explaining to Tamsin a few days ago how a scratch in Philip's paintwork really wasn't your style,' Elin said.

'Sounded cool,' Tamsin said.

Sitting down to the table, coffee mug in hand, Bede raised his eyebrows. 'Really?'

'I wish I could've been there. It must've been great to feel you're really doing something.'

'Were we?'

'You've gotta let me know next time – like, the next Frack-Free Foxover protest – and I'll join you.'

Bede exchanged a look with Elin. 'I sincerely hope it won't get that far. That the local authority will see sense before it gets to large-scale protesting. If it has to be, I won't let the side down, but in general I prefer to put my energy into all we've got going here.'

'Talking of which,' Elin said, beckoning to Tamsin, 'we can't sit around all day. You can put the world to rights later. Right now, there's a greenhouse full of plants calling.'

That evening, Elin pedalled her way along the lane, trying to ignore the drizzle borne on the insistent wind and the scattered puddles weakly illuminated by the beam of her bike light. After her afternoon shift she'd stayed behind to help with redecorating the shop, and felt too tired to call in the pub for a chat with Bede and the regulars. The sky to the west was heavy and grey. If it weren't for the clouds, it would still be light. It hadn't felt like a proper spring evening for weeks – or maybe spring would be like this from now on? If Bede had said that, she'd have told him off for being negative.

A gust swelled the treetops as she pedalled past Holtwood. Even the pheasants were silent. The gloomy weather and forbidding yellow signs made her angry. She was too tired right then, but she'd come back in the morning with their flyers. It felt petty. She made herself feel better by thinking she could combine it with a walk beyond the woods to check for signs of activity. While she stopped short of believing in outright corruption, she still didn't trust Northcote, or the contractors, Prospect G, not to be engaged in inappropriate preparatory work.

As she left the woodland behind, a lone crow flapped low overhead, looking abashed as though it were late home without phoning through. Elin wondered what had got into her.

In the warmth of the kitchen, Kip leapt up at her as if she'd been gone for days. She muttered nonsense words of reassurance and stood in the back doorway shivering as he went nosing busily around the yard. A glance at the clock told her Bede would be in the Horseshoes for at least another hour. Kip curled up beside her on the sofa as she picked up her book, ready to escape to someone else's world. Her mug of hot chocolate and the crackling fire began to lull her.

The phone rang and jolted her awake. The dog ignored it and she was tempted to do the same. If it was important they'd leave a message. But it was after eleven – the caller must really want something to be ringing at this time. She grabbed the handset, interrupting the answer machine as it began to cut in.

'Tamsin! Do you know what time it is?'

'Sorry. This is important. Elin, please, can you get down here? We...we don't know what to do.'

Her irritation gave way to a hollow fear.

'What's wrong? Where are you?'

'On the lane by Holtwood. Lauren was giving me a lift home and we saw... She's phoning an ambulance and I had to phone you. Elin, he's just lying there! *I don't know what to do!*'

She was on the verge of tears.

'Who, Tamsin? What's happened?'

Elin's hands shook as she jabbed the telephone off, grabbed her still-damp coat and ran out. Rain lashed the windscreen faster than the wipers could clear it. As she rounded the corner where the woods began, she thought momentarily of that solitary crow.

The two girls were standing guard over a huddled shape at the side of the lane. Elin jerked to a halt in the middle of the road. The first thing she saw was a shiny pink raincoat draped incongruously over his shoulders. The wrongness swelled and threatened to engulf her as she ran over and knelt by his head.

'Bede?'

No response. She clutched at his hand and absently brushed a strand of hair from his face. He was breathing. She should have been reassured by that. She said his name again.

'The ambulance and the police are on their way,' Tamsin said. Elin looked up reluctantly. 'We didn't want to move him or the bike in case...you know...'

'It's OK,' Elin said. 'There's a blanket in the back of my car, and a groundsheet. Can you—'

Tamsin was on her way before the words were out, clearly relieved to be able to do something. Elin bundled her own coat into a pillow and gently eased it beneath his head, hoping the blood pooled at his temple was only from the graze she could see. The lack of response in his familiar features terrified her. She tried to extricate the bike from his leg, but soon gave up. She felt as helpless as the girls.

Tamsin returned with the blanket and groundsheet and Elin covered him over. She handed her the pink raincoat, then tried again to talk to Bede, all the while clutching his hand.

'What happened?' she asked the girls.

'We came round the bend and saw him lying there. Lauren just managed to stop in time. She only passed her test last month. This is one of the first nights… Sorry.'

Elin couldn't help glancing at the girls' car for any sign of an impact, then immediately felt guilty for suspecting them.

'What time was it?'

'Sorry,' Tamsin said, 'I never looked.'

'Just after ten past eleven.' Her friend spoke for the first time. 'I remember the clock showed 11:11 as we were going through the village. We commented on it.'

'Well remembered. Did you see him leave the pub? Or anyone else?'

'Sorry,' Tamsin said again. 'A crowd of us left early to watch a film at Ryan's. Then I wanted to get back 'cause we're supposed to be making an early start tomorrow…' Her eyes filled with tears. She looked down at Bede. 'I'm glad we left when we did.'

Elin gripped Bede's hand as she caught a glimpse of headlights and heard an approaching engine. The blue light flashed eerily, lighting up the hedgerows in a macabre dance.

A show of politeness

Tap, tap, tap…

He'd been hammering something. With Elin. Where was she now? Some stupid argument; something was wrong. He realised he was in a hospital ward, nothing else, no context, no reason. Where was she? He closed his eyes. It felt wrong to think.

He became aware again, a vague headache hovering beneath the surface but the gap in his life filling itself in. Herding a gaggle of escaped sheep with Frank Barnham. Helping repair the hedge. Fixing timbers together to form the frame for the caravan. Yes, the hammering. Elin smiling. Maybe there was nothing wrong after all. Warm relief washed over him. He opened his eyes, saw the hospital room again. Closed them in denial.

'Bede?'

Sitting in their kitchen, chatting with her and the girl… Tamsin, that was it. He dared to look, saw Elin sitting by the bed, felt her squeeze his hand. She felt warm. Which meant he must be cold.

'Thank goodness you're all right,' she said.

'Am I? Are you?'

'Of course I am. You…you will be.'

'What? What's happened?'

'Don't worry for now. Just…'

'That's making me worry.' He looked around, saw his leg cradled and raised. Realised there was a pain as dull as the one in his head coming from his foot. Painkillers must be damping it. A drip fed a cannula in the back of the hand she was cradling gently. The other arm was immobilised in a brace. He fought down the fear. 'Don't mess about, El. Tell me.'

She glanced at the door, then back to him. 'You were knocked off your bike. On your way home from work.'

'Work? With Steve? That was days ago, wasn't it?'

'No, not that. At the Horseshoes. Late last night.'

The ache nagged and he closed his eyes. 'What's wrong with me?'

He waved the hand she was still holding towards his feet.

'You...you've got a broken ankle. The way you fell. They're going to operate, set it as soon as you're ready to take the anaesthetic. Shouldn't be too long now you're awake.' She stroked his hand with her thumb. 'Your arm... you broke your wrist as well. Presumably sticking your hand out to cushion the impact. It's a clean fracture, tiny bone – nowhere near as bad as the ankle. They'll put it in a cast when they do your leg.'

Instinctively, he braced himself with his elbows and shifted his left leg. The pain in his foot intensified, as did the ache from his left wrist. He made himself relax.

'So...how did it happen?'

From the expression on her face, he almost felt like telling *her* not to worry.

'We don't know. Hit-and-run. The bike was buckled – you were hit. The police found a car burnt out on the Halbury road. It was stolen – joyriders, probably. They want to talk to you when you feel ready. Do you remember anything? Anything at all?'

He closed his eyes; saw the scene in their kitchen. Whenever that was. It didn't lead anywhere. The headache was getting worse. He raised his hand, felt a dressing at his temple.

'Maybe you'll remember to wear your cycle helmet next time,' she said, clearly trying to sound light-hearted about it.

'On my feet?'

'Not funny.' She smiled all the same.

'Seriously, I can handle a headache, but how long's this going to take? What about Alderleat, what about the Sunny Days job? I'm not going to be much use to anyone on crutches.'

She indicated his arm. 'You'll have to rely on my wheelchair driving skills to begin with.' She cut off his expletive. 'You're supposed to rest anyway after concussion.'

'The pub? We can't afford—'

'We'll sort it all out. For now I'm just glad you're here and talking to me. It's been hell today.'

A nurse came over and cheerfully introduced herself. Bede forced a smile as she asked him how he was and went through a series of routine checks, but hoped she wouldn't chat more than necessary. Others might find small talk reassuring, but Elin was the only one he could face speaking to. The nurse handed him a glass of water; he realised how dry his mouth had been.

'Steady, take it gradually at first. Do you feel like something to eat?'

No, I feel like roadkill. He stared into the water glass.

'Bede…' Elin prompted.

'Yeah, suppose I ought to try something.' He waved the empty glass towards the over-bed table and she took it from him. 'Vegetarian,' he added.

'You've missed lunch but I'll see what I can find you.'

Elin looked between him and the nurse. 'That'd be lovely, thanks.'

Bede thought to himself that lying in a hospital bed with

a worsening headache and a smashed foot was a perfect excuse for forgetting to say please.

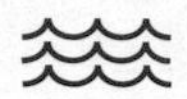

'Thanks for all this. I really appreciate it.'

Elin straightened up, the sofa bed finally manoeuvred into place, and Carole helped her extend it. The small dining room looked cramped, the table and chairs pushed to one side, but she really hadn't the energy to move anything else.

'I told you,' Carole said as she flapped a sheet and watched it float gracefully down into place, 'you should have got a couple of lads from the Horseshoes to give him a fireman's lift up to the bedroom. At least he'd be stuck up there and forced to rest.'

'He'd only lie there wasting energy devising escape strategies. Then fall down the stairs trying, and make things worse. Thank goodness for the downstairs shower-room.' Elin positioned the pillows and straightened the duvet. 'There, that's about done. I really shouldn't second-guess him; he'll probably amaze me and turn out to be the model patient.'

'You just keep believing he will – you need to stay optimistic.' Carole followed her through to the kitchen and began tidying the breakfast things, waving away Elin's protests. 'You'd better be on your way soon. Once you're gone I'll go out to the greenhouse and help myself to what we need for the shop. I'll rearrange the rota to cover for you.'

'Thanks. You must have—'

'It's fine. And if you're not back, I'll call round this evening – chickens, Kip…'

Elin found her calm efficiency soothing. 'I can't tell you how grateful I am.'

'People turn to you often enough, Elin. It's my turn now – I'll do anything I can to help. This is such a shitty thing to have happened.'

'What do you think did happen?' Elin glanced at her then stared out of the window.

'The police said it was joyriders, didn't they?'

'Yes, but…'

'What?'

'They haven't spoken to Philip Northcote yet.'

Carole clattered some dishes on the draining-board. 'Philip? Why on earth would you think he had anything to do with it?'

'Oh, it doesn't matter.'

'You can't be serious. Has Bede done something else to piss him off?'

'Why does everyone always suspect Bede?' Elin grabbed a cloth and scrubbed at the table as if she could wipe away the recent events.

'I don't. Sorry. I meant because he's a leading light in the campaign.'

Elin decided to give her clumsy change of tack the benefit of the doubt. 'He dropped a careless hint about bribery and corruption last week. So it could have been some kind of warning.'

'Honestly, Elin! Whatever Philip's views, surely you can't believe he'd actually do something like that.'

'It could've turned out worse than he intended. Or he could've employed someone.'

'Bloody hell, girl, you want to be careful what you say.'

Elin felt defensive. 'We want to know what happened.'

'Bede was unlucky, that's all.'

As she dried the last of the pots, Elin heard a car pull up outside and glanced out of the window. 'Silvan.'

She went to open the door.

'Hi.' He indicated his muddy boots and hovered on the doorstep. 'Tammy told me at the weekend what happened. She's really worried; asked me to tell you she'll be round as soon as she can. I thought I'd call myself to see how the man is.'

'I'm just off to the hospital to find out,' Elin said.

'That bad? He's still in?'

'It was a while before they could set his ankle, and in any case, he had concussion so they wanted to keep an eye on him for a couple of days.'

'What a bummer,' Silvan said. Carole looked unsure what to make of him. 'Does he play draughts? Cards? Tell him I'll be round. We need to keep that genius brain exercised.'

Elin snorted. 'Please don't go inflating his ego. But thanks for the offer; good idea. He's meant to rest, but I doubt he'll be very good at enforced inactivity. I'm sure he'll be pleased to see you.'

She watched him go, then turned back inside to Carole's inquisitively-raised eyebrows. 'He seems to have his feet under the table.'

'He's called by a few times,' Elin said. 'Seems OK. It was nice of him to come.'

'That's not what I meant. I take it "Tammy" is Kate's Tamsin?'

Elin nodded.

'Since when?'

'Not long. They were supposed to be going to the coast together last Sunday but with all the drama they hardly got to see each other, so she told me.'

'I can't imagine Kate's very happy. He's a good few years older than Tamsin, isn't he?'

'And hardly Kate's idea of a nice young man.' Elin smiled, then narrowed her eyes. 'Actually, I don't think she knows. Though I guess it won't be long now before she does.'

'You malign me,' Carole said. 'I'm the soul of discretion. About your Northcote hints, too, don't worry. Anyway you'd best be off.' She glanced at the clock with a conspiratorial wink. 'Damn. Even if I give you a lift to the village you'll have missed the bus. You'll have to take the car.'

'Don't be like that. It's *unnecessary* journeys we object to.'

Carole smiled as if indulging a favourite child. 'In oversized vehicles like mine.'

'I didn't say—'

'*He* has. More than once. Oh, sorry I mentioned it. Time to get moving.'

Elin gathered up a pile of papers and books from the living-room floor to provide a clear passage for the wheelchair the occupational therapist had offered to obtain for him. She stood for a moment, inexplicably lost, until Carole ushered her out.

'It's not like you to fret. Come on, he'll be waiting for you.'

Bede sat listening to the comforting sounds of Elin pottering in the kitchen. Kip gazed up at him, nose in his lap, calmer now. He'd hindered their awkward progress into the house by leaping up at the wheelchair as though his master had been gone for weeks, sniffing at the plaster cast from knee to toe, looking suspiciously as though he were about to mark it as his own. Bede gazed at the stiff lump that was his leg, the dull ache frustratingly encased out of reach, ironically less painful than the more minor injury of his wrist.

He thought about the weeks to come. Steve had phoned to express his sympathy and to reassure Bede that even if he was laid up for a while, he could still be involved with their new project, doing the calculations, dimensioning and design while Steve saw to the practical side. He'd probably intended to make him feel better, but in fact he felt trapped – however much he enjoyed all aspects of a project and its challenges, the prospect of being cooped up indoors filled him with claustrophobic horror.

It was still hard to shake off the sense that he could somehow turn the clock back to the time, only a few days ago, when he'd been unharmed. Try as he might, he could only retrace the steps of his life as far as Saturday morning. Brian had phoned, talked him through the evening at work, described every detail of who was in the pub, snatches of conversation, songs that had played in the background.

That little corner of memory seemed lost to the mental bruise of concussion and, for now at least, he simply had to accept that it was a part of his life that had vanished forever, together with any clues it might contain about the vehicle that had floored him or the identity of its occupants. Common sense said it was the burnt-out car abandoned by joyriders on the outskirts of Halbury, and there was little chance of them being traced, but was common sense enough? It felt deliberate. Of course it did! He shook his head. No way did a vague feeling amount to insightful intuition. This was an accident, like Joe's death had been an accident.

And there he was – full circle. Try as he might, he couldn't accept either.

He reached for the book he'd been reading and found his

place. The sound of Elin's voice triggered the swooping awakening of someone who hadn't realised he'd fallen asleep.

'Dozed off?' she said as she came in with a lap tray.

They'd said fatigue was perfectly natural after a trauma like this, as much to be expected as momentary blackouts, memory loss and headaches, but it made him feel guilty and inadequate. She gave him a don't-worry-about-it smile as she carefully positioned the tray on his thighs and went to fetch her own. He noticed she'd cut up the pie. Without fuss. He picked up his fork. At least it was his right hand that was still working; he should be thankful for small mercies.

He smiled his gratitude, already tucking in, as she sat in the armchair opposite him. No sooner had she settled than the doorbell rang.

'Timing.' Rolling his eyes, he motioned her to stay where she was and they yelled *Come in!* in loud unison.

Tamsin appeared, clutching a large card, a box of chocolates and a bunch of flowers. 'Oh, you're eating, sorry – d'you want me to come back later? You weren't here when I got back from school and then it was like dinner time and this is the first chance I've had… Didn't know if flowers were right for a fella but anyway I'm sure Elin'll like them if you don't. From our garden. Shit, look at you. You poor thing. Well, it's a relief after Saturday night, but, you know…' She caught Elin's eye and smiled self-consciously. 'Oops, talking too much.'

'Saves me having to think of the right response.' Bede smiled back. 'Nice flowers, thank you. Hope you don't mind watching us eat.'

'Can you do us a favour?' Elin said. 'You'll find a vase somewhere in the kitchen…'

Tamsin vanished and a little later appeared with the

flowers prettily arranged. She perched on the edge of a chair until they'd finished eating, then cleared away the plates with equally keen efficiency. They heard another knock at the door as she reached the kitchen.

'I've never felt so popular,' Bede muttered.

'Don't flatter yourself,' Elin said. 'They're all coming to make sure I'm coping with you.'

He was surprised to see Silvan walk in.

'Hiya,' he said, flopping down on the sofa. 'Did Elin tell you I called this morning? She said you'd probably be home tonight. Just came to see how you were.'

Bede gestured with the hand that wasn't held captive. 'Never better, mate, never better.'

He ignored the look Elin gave him. Silvan seemed unperturbed. As he asked if they knew anything about what had happened, Bede wondered how many times he was going to have to explain, and for how long he could continue to repeat himself with a show of politeness. Maybe he should write it down, get a T-shirt printed. He gave the briefest account of the police's joyrider story and his own lack of recall. 'I can't help wondering…'

Silvan flicked his eyes in Tamsin's direction with a subtle shake of his head.

'Were you in the Horseshoes?' Bede said. 'Did you see anything?'

'I was back in Brum for a No Surrender gig, wasn't I?'

He got out his phone and showed them a few pictures. Bede gave them a cursory glance – Silvan looked good on stage but it was pretty pointless without the audio.

'Wish you could've been there,' Silvan said. 'I mean, I hope you'd have been into the music of course – but practically, if you'd hadn't been in Foxover, you wouldn't have had all this.'

Elin got up and offered to make them a coffee. Bede felt sleep closing in on him. It was ridiculous; he'd been dozing on and off all day.

'You're welcome to stay,' he said, 'but sleep's my default setting at the moment. So please don't be offended if I give you my full and undivided attention with my eyes closed.'

'I think that's a subtle way of saying "another time", yeah?' Silvan grinned. He glanced at them both. 'Anything we can do to help before we go?'

We. Bede glanced at Tamsin. So it was already that serious. He was tempted to decline the offer, but Elin looked done in and, suppressing a sigh, he decided it was worth the discomfort and embarrassment of being manhandled into bed by near-strangers to save her the effort.

Being seen like this

For the next few days, Bede slept most of the time, as though his battered body and mind were forcing him to listen to reason and rest. When awake, he was as irascible a patient as Elin had feared, obviously trying his damnedest not to take it out on her, but summoning a cloud down around them both all the same. She could hardly blame him; even though the painkillers dulled the worst of the pain from his injuries, they weren't enough for the occasional headaches, at times enough to wake him, and at others following some strange irrelevant pronouncement he couldn't afterwards remember making.

The police were convinced it was joyriders and soon abandoned the line of enquiry that they might have been in someone's employ. Bede veered between anger, frustration and apathy, and to cap it all, his usual safety valve of long, solitary walks was denied him.

He apologised for not being able to help around the house, but managed to make it sound like he was drawing attention to his incapacity – look what I'm reduced to; I can't even wash up! She was reminded increasingly of the bleak weeks and months following Joe's death; the dark tunnel they'd only recently emerged from. People – Fran, Carole, her sister – had wondered at the time why he, or both of them, hadn't sought professional help. Faced with the memory of his hurt and anger when she'd broached the subject – the way he took it as criticism, his insistence he wouldn't tell a stranger anything he couldn't tell her – she intended to wait a while longer this time before suggesting he took up the offer of counselling.

By the end of the week he insisted on being taken out to the workshop. Elin was worried. Only that morning, over breakfast, he'd fixed her with a stare and said, 'You really shouldn't attach the red filament to that'– then frowned, looking afraid, as she questioned it and he failed to recall having spoken.

She wondered if the workshop was a safe place for him to be. Indignant at the implication of incompetence, he nevertheless agreed not to go near any machine tools and they decided to trust his instincts and sense of self-preservation. She made sure the phone was within reach on the bench, reminding herself that he wasn't a helpless infant but an intelligent, resourceful adult who happened to have a broken ankle and wrist, and was afflicted by occasional blackouts; if he somehow contrived to fall, the very suggestion of which he took as a personal insult, he would be quite capable of finding a solution, or simply waiting if it came to it.

After a busy morning at the shop, she cycled back home for lunch in a flurry of imaginary scenarios, but as she opened the workshop door, he simply looked up at her cheerfully over his black-rimmed glasses.

'Perfect timing. You can help me get this in place.'

He'd literally single-handedly fitted a wheel to an electric motor from an old school project and adapted it to latch into brackets he had ready to fix to the front of his wheelchair. He'd grumbled about the small wheels before realising his wrist was in no condition to propel himself anyway, and she had to smile at his response to the prospect of relying on someone to push it during the weeks before he was ready for crutches. The thought of defacing social services' property bothered her but he assured her he'd make it good afterwards if anyone complained.

Perched on a beam, leg sticking out at a cumbersome angle, he munched the sandwiches she'd brought and directed her in fitting first the brackets, then the motor. Elin sensed him keeping his instructions tactfully light – she respected his expertise but he'd long since learned not to patronise her. He fidgeted like a little boy on Christmas Eve as she attached the makeshift controls, and she was pleased to see he was grudgingly impressed. She indulged him as he proclaimed how he'd proved conclusively that his unruly stock of old and reclaimed parts was not mere hoarding. To preserve her peace of mind, she tried not to wonder how he'd manoeuvred the clunky wheelchair across the room to rummage through it.

The finished contraption whirred like a robot in an old low-budget sci-fi film, and they both laughed as he performed a few practice laps of the limited space. As he tentatively ascended and descended the ramp and platform she'd borrowed from the village hall and rigged up for him behind the workbench, the serious concentration on his face incongruously conveyed joy at his reclaimed independence.

When she came in later that afternoon to find him with his head slumped on folded arms on the bench, he didn't even try to deny his impromptu nap.

'So,' he said cheerfully, 'shall we celebrate tonight?'

'Celebrate?'

'Mobility. Life going on.' Bede ruffled Kip's fur. The dog had only just accepted the whirring wheelchair and still eyed him with suspicion. 'It's music night at the Horseshoes, isn't it?'

Elin was not only pleased by the prospect of an evening

out, but relieved at the turning of another corner. One of his frequent complaints during the recent days of confinement and sleep had been embarrassment at 'being seen like this', and she'd dreaded weeks of self-imposed exile from the world.

'Let's go the whole hog and have a meal,' she said. 'Spare you the guilt about not washing up.'

'Deal.'

He extended his hand and they shook in mock formality. He held onto hers for a moment longer than necessary.

As she helped him shower and change, every gesture of support, every move to help him to his feet in a clumsy stand became an excuse to linger, to share an affectionate hug and a kiss. Since the accident, he'd been unusually demonstrative, as if trying to make up for his blacker moods. Despite the circumstances, and the moods, she liked it.

It was a fine evening and they arrived at the Horseshoes to see Tamsin and Silvan sitting at a table in the garden with several of the regular crowd. They came over, offering welcome help in negotiating the uneven threshold and steps to which they'd never before given a second thought. A table was free near the performance area; joined by Tamsin's friend Lauren, they settled around it with Bede alongside a wall, where he was out of danger of his leg being knocked. Silvan went to help Gareth set up the sound system and Brian came over with their drinks.

'Good to see you, Eco. Hurry up and get better; we're missing you. Just give me a wave when you want a refill. There's a few in for you behind the bar.'

No sooner had Brian left to take their food order to the kitchen than Elin noticed Bede's eyes narrow. She followed his gaze and her heart sank as she saw Philip Northcote crossing the pub towards them.

'Just when I was beginning to enjoy the evening,' Bede muttered.

'Might as well get it over with.' She squeezed his hand.

Philip reached their table and, ignoring the spare seat Elin indicated, stood towering over them. 'What do you think you're playing at now?'

'Not too bad, thanks for asking,' Bede replied steadily. 'Could've been worse.'

'I doubt either of us wants to waste time on pleasantries.' Normally Bede stood a head taller than Philip, but in his wheelchair Elin thought he looked vulnerable and cornered. Despite the steely determination in his eyes, she felt protective as Philip continued. 'I've wasted enough hours of my valuable time as it is, being grilled by the police and having my car, every vehicle belonging to the shoot and even my commercial fleet examined for marks that indicate knocking a bloke off his bike. I wonder why – I was away over the weekend, for God's sake.'

'Oh, were you? Where?'

'A colleague's wedding, not that it's any of your business. I have alibis, and the police are satisfied with them. They didn't find a thing, of course, but I can do without you making false accusations for the fun of it.'

'False accusations.' Bede's eyes flashed fire. 'I've had a few directed my way recently. No harm in returning the favour, hey? Oh, sorry, I forget that my time isn't valuable. Not in the sense of distorting the local ecosystem so toffs can roam the countryside killing birds for fun. Or scheming to destroy our land for a quick fix of climate-wrecking fossil fuels. But, you know what? Perhaps there are ways of measuring "valuable" that don't involve stockpiling wealth so you can—'

'Give it a rest. You do realise that with every pronouncement you're digging your own grave?'

Bede patted the arm of the wheelchair, still without relinquishing eye contact. 'Which someone's trying their damnedest to put me in.'

Philip took a step closer, placing a hand on the table and leaning across it. Elin tensed and looked around for Silvan. He was still chatting to Gareth; she tried to catch his eye. She turned back to intervene, but Philip got in first.

'You want to be careful how far you take your slander.' He held up a hand to silence Bede's protest. 'It won't do you any good. I'm giving a valuable boost to the local economy and doing my share to help this country's energy situation, however unpopular that may make me in some quarters. There are plenty of people who appreciate and support what I'm doing. I wouldn't dream of resorting to violence, or employing someone to do it on my behalf, and it's preposterous that you could even begin to think I might.' He turned to Tamsin. 'I'm surprised to see you here. Aren't you in the middle of exams?'

'Only got a few more. They're days away. We've got to have a break now and then.'

'Does your mother know where you are?'

Tamsin glanced in silence at Lauren, making it transparently obvious where she was meant to be.

'I thought not,' Philip said. 'If you go now, there'll be no need for me to tell her.'

'Oh, leave her alone!' Elin snapped. 'Isn't bullying a man in a wheelchair enough for you?'

'Bullying?' Philip gave a snort of contempt. 'He's quite capable of looking after himself. She, on the other hand, obviously needs a bit of guidance – more than she's getting from her so-called friends.'

Bede laughed harshly. 'What gives you the right to tell

her what she can and can't do? The fact that you're shagging her mother?'

Philip lurched towards him, knocking the table against his wheelchair.

Bede gasped in pain. 'Wouldn't dream of violence, hey?'

Elin reached a hand out to grasp Philip's arm. He shook her off, knocking over a full pint glass that crashed into splinters on the quarry-tiled floor. Tamsin saved a second glass, but the contents joined the cocktail spreading around their feet and soaking their legs. The whole pub froze in a moment's stunned silence. Silvan looked across, frowning, as Brian hurried towards them.

'Enough! What the hell's going on?' He looked between them, glancing at Elin with a flicker of sympathy as he did so. 'Just sort out your bloody differences elsewhere, will you? I've no idea what this is about, and I don't want to know.' Elin seriously doubted both claims. 'But stay away from each other while you're in here. If there's the slightest hint of any more trouble I'm chucking the lot of you out.'

Philip glared at Brian and made his way in stony silence back to his table, where he was greeted with muted encouragement by his cronies. Before he was out of earshot, Bede apologised profusely for the mess and his inability to help clear it up.

Elin smiled to herself. He always did have to have the last word.

Stranded

Waking to another day in his makeshift quarters in the dining room, Bede blinked at a ray of sunlight through a chink in the curtain. The bedclothes had slipped and the beer stains on his cast brought it all back. He closed his eyes, wincing from the memory as much as his headache. A succession of people had come over to their table with comments ranging from sympathy and support to awkwardly pretending either his accident or the scene with Philip hadn't happened. The show of friendship had been heartening and the music good, especially Elin's singing, but the evening had been soured from the start and he'd spent the whole time drinking too much while wishing they could simply go home.

And now here he was, the quality of the light suggesting that almost a morning had passed in useless inactivity. Add to that the countless wasted hours and days since the accident. Brooding on how much of that time he'd spent sleeping, he reached for the note on the bedside table. Elin was in the greenhouse. He knew she had a lot to do at the shop, and wondered irritably why she hadn't woken him sooner so she could get him sorted and be on her way. Taking a deep breath, he silently played through the frustration and criticism so he could get it out of his system and not upset her by voicing it. Maybe he could get away without disturbing her at all.

Thinking of the whole damn palaver of simple routines like shifting himself from the bed to the chair without overbalancing or struggling to get dressed, fill the kettle and make coffee with one hand, he gave in and picked up the phone.

A short while later, he was sitting at the breakfast table having packed Elin off to the shop, insisting as tactfully as he could that, now he was up, he could manage. The need to get out in the fresh air, clear his head, became overwhelming. A walk. A bloody trundle, he corrected himself. He wouldn't have any muscles left by the time this was over.

However he managed to get there, the river was beckoning. He called Kip, who seemed to have forgiven him for turning into a whirring automaton, wasted a few more moments jabbing with a broom handle to dislodge the dog's lead from a shoulder-level coat hook, and set off. Even pulling the door closed behind him was a major operation.

After fastening the lead to the arm of the chair, hoping Kip would remember what a well-trained, obedient dog he was, Bede set off. He soon saw that, although yesterday had been fine, the recent rain meant the gateway to their willow field was waterlogged, as was the track down the side. He may have devised mobility for himself, but an all-terrain model was a little ambitious. Not feeling sociable enough for Foxover, he turned in the opposite direction, making for the riverside picnic area down the Halbury lane. It was sure to be deserted on a grey Thursday morning.

From his unaccustomed perspective, the road seemed a maze of puddles and potholes to be dodged. Once safely past Kate's drive, having noted gratefully the absence of parked cars outside the house, he took his fingers from the controls and halted. The brief pause in the irritating whine of the motor allowed the voice of the river to reach him.

Bede let the dog loose and, hardly aware of the thin drizzle whipped up by the wind, gazed out across fields and hedgerows to the glimpse of dull pewter as the river reflected the flat grey sky above. The sun that had woken him earlier had vanished, but the wind in his hair and the call of the water were already working their magic.

Above the rushing of the river and hushing of the saturated wind, he became aware of another sound: the white noise of an approaching car's tyres. Bede froze. He wanted to look round, but, as if held fast in the treacle fingers of a nightmare, couldn't move. He saw a gateway up ahead; willed his thumb to press the drive button. It wouldn't obey. He braced himself for the impact, rain-hunched shoulders brought even closer to his ears. He saw himself in the ditch, life and blood seeping from him. Finishing the job that had been started nearly two weeks ago.

The car swished past, slowing and skirting by him. He didn't see a face, but thought he saw a movement on the passenger side. He wanted to wave back, but his white-knuckled hand still refused to obey. His heart thumped in terror as the car slowed and stopped, red brake lights giving way to white reversing lights as it bore down on him. He closed his eyes.

'Are you OK?'

Angie's voice. Feeling utterly stupid, he blinked and managed to stammer out something about going for a walk. It seemed to satisfy her and they went on their way.

Once they were gone, he managed somehow to reach the next bend, where the road widened to form a gravelly layby. His heart was pounding, his whole body shaking. He heard another vehicle, this time approaching from the Halbury direction. He tensed again, blackness clouding the edge of his vision. Kip came bounding up; Bede leaned forward and grabbed his collar, allowing the wind to drive his hair across his face, ashamed of the car's occupants seeing the terror there as he waited for them to swerve and drive straight at him.

As the noise of the unseen car faded and his frayed nerves began to settle, he steeled himself against a growing headache. A van and another car passed and his irrational terror was no less. He felt like a wreck. A car crash, ha ha. Filled with self-loathing, he forced himself to admit that this…this shambolic outing bore no resemblance to the wild abandon and release of tension he got from striding out across the fields. Abandon. Yes, abandon the idea. With any luck he could get home before another vehicle came past. Or maybe the next really would be the one with his name on the bull bars.

He shook his head, scattering drops of drizzle, and manoeuvred the wheelchair round to face home. It caught in a rut and jolted; with a serious effort of balance, he managed to stay upright. He jabbed the controls desperately but it refused to move, forwards or backwards. The whirring stopped abruptly. With hollow despair, he realised he'd just discovered the range of the battery. He managed to manoeuvre himself upright and behind it, grab one handle and lean on the other with his plastered arm, to use it as a walking frame. He hopped. It almost tipped. The lane towards the house appeared endless. He collapsed back into the seat.

Cursing himself for not charging it last night, for failing to think about it before setting out…just cursing the whole fucking situation, he realised he'd have to disturb Elin – again. Even before his hand felt the emptiness of his pocket, he had a clear mental image of the mobile lying by the side of the bed. Please no. An increasingly frantic search through pockets and down the sides of the seat cushion only confirmed it.

In desperation, he sent Kip homeward. At first the dog ran in the right direction, but was soon distracted by an investigation of the roadside hedge.

'Home! Fetch Elin!'

As Kip vanished out of sight round the bend, Bede had no illusions of his dog running to the village in some Lassie-style rescue, but at least Elin would see him alone in the yard when she got home and… When would she be home? The wind was gusting harder and the mildly uncomfortable drizzle was fast intensifying to proper rain. He remembered he wasn't supposed to get the cast on his useless leg wet. He managed to extricate himself from his coat, covered the cast and settled in, shivering, to wait. The ache in his wrist and ankle, together with the headache, slowly worsened with the creeping cold, and he berated himself for his misplaced pride earlier when he'd thought that taking a painkiller was giving in.

He had no idea how much time had passed – maybe he'd done his amazing fall-asleep-anywhere thing – when he heard another vehicle approaching. The thought of welcome rescue outweighed the conviction that he was about to be rammed into the hedge, and he raised a hand to flag it down. As it rounded the bend, his heart jolted as he recognised, through the now driving rain, the jeep he'd seen more than once churning up the tracks around the pheasant pens in Holtwood.

It was a busy morning in the shop, but Elin found time to try ringing Bede a couple of times. He'd been feeling down that morning, hardly surprising given the amount he'd drunk the night before, and she just wanted to hear his voice. She was mildly surprised when his phone went to voicemail both times, and the second time she tried the house phone. No answer. There was an extension by his bench in the workshop and he wouldn't be outside in rain like this. It was enough to send her home for lunch, despite the sandwich she'd left ready for him in the kitchen.

As she headed down the lane towards Alderleat, she was surprised to see smoke coming from the chimney. The summer rain lent a chill to the air, but she doubted it was cold enough indoors for Bede to light a fire. Even in his current condition he'd stubbornly pile on an extra blanket rather than waste fuel at this time of year. It was pointless arguing with him about the fine distinctions between *waste, use* and *need* at a time like this.

She called his name as she entered. Only Kip responded. She went through and saw Bede laid out on the sofa beneath a duvet, with pillows brought through from his bed. Elin glanced at the glow of the fire in the stove, the flames flickering in a way that indicated it had not been lit for very long. A faint smell of smoke tinged the air. Not wood smoke. Concerned by the pallor of his skin, she touched his forehead; he felt cold. She frowned – the hint of smoke was on him, too – said his name, shook him gently. He stirred.

'Time is it?'

'About one o'clock,' she said.

'Sorry. Didn't sleep too well last night. Need to catch up.'

'Stop apologising for resting.' His hair was damp and there was a heap of wet clothes on the floor. 'Have you been out?'

'Tell you later.'

She quickly felt his hands, free foot and toes at the end

of the cast. They felt cold but within reason. She adjusted the duvet, removed the damp pillow and replaced it with a towel-wrapped cushion. He waved her away.

'Please. Stop fussing.' He turned his head and frowned. 'What's going on? What've you lit the fire for? It's not cold, it's the start of bloody summer!'

'It was already lit. I thought you—'

'How d'you think I could've done that? Stop fussing over me.'

She flung the damp pillow down by the fire to dry and marched into the kitchen. Grabbing a glass of water and the lunch she'd made him earlier, she slammed them down on the coffee table next to him, only just restraining herself from sticking the dog's nose in the sandwiches. Turning to go, she caught sight of the wheelchair across the room, out of his reach. However it had got there, let it stay. God forbid she should fuss.

'See you this evening.'

'Bye, love,' he murmured. 'Sorry.'

Sorry! She was almost out of the door when she saw the note by the kettle.

Hi Ellen,
Found Bede stranded at the side of the road!!
Seems OK, just tired. Says he wanted to get out.
He can explain when he wakes. Sorry I couldn't stay but had to get back to work - I'm in deep enough shit as it is.
Will try & call round this evening to see how u both are.
Silvan

She went back through to the living room.

'What's this about Silvan finding you at the side of the road?' she said more gently.

'What?' He opened his eyes. 'I went for a walk. Battery ran out. Did he bring the charger through from the workshop? We need to remember to charge it.' He stirred. 'I'm sorry Elin, I forgot – must've been him lit the fire. I shouldn't have said that. About fussing. Come here. Sorry.'

He reached out. She knelt by the sofa and held him, allowing her annoyance to subside.

'Why didn't you call me?'

'Forgot the phone. Can't even get that right. Sorry again. You'd better get back. Thanks for…you know.'

On her way out, she fetched the phone from the side of the bed and put it alongside his lunch. He was already breathing to a sleeper's rhythm, his face relaxed in the expression she found it impossible to stay angry with.

The doorbell rang. Elin sighed. She'd been hoping that 'try and call round this evening' was merely a stock phrase, and Silvan wouldn't actually appear. It had been a long day.

'Bede's asleep, but come in for a couple of minutes anyway. Thanks for helping this morning.'

She hoped 'couple of minutes' would be a big enough hint, but Silvan produced a bottle of wine from the canvas satchel that was almost a part of him and plonked it on the kitchen table.

'You look like you need this.'

'No thanks. It's sweet of you, but…'

'Go on, you deserve it. Is he going to join us? I can give him a hand—'

'I don't want to wake him.' Feeling churlish but

determined, she sat at the table without fetching glasses or moving to open the bottle.

Silvan's account of that morning's rescue began similarly enough to Bede's until he said, 'You know what, Elin? He accused me of driving right at him. Honestly, he had this look on his face when I got out of the jeep, pushed me away and started yelling at me, what the fuck was I playing at, thought I was supposed to be his mate and all that. He calmed down eventually, but he was still shaking like crazy. Could've been the cold. I'm sure it was, partly – him sitting there without his coat, the nutter – but he really worried me. Did he say anything to you?'

Elin shook her head. 'I'm sure it was nothing personal.'

Silvan traced the pattern on the label of the bottle with his finger. 'I did the right thing, didn't I? He seemed frozen through and I couldn't just leave him without a fire. He was acting a bit weird at first, but I sorted him out and he seemed fine by the time I left. I haven't got your number.'

'Thanks for everything.' She looked at him sternly. 'Hope you don't mind me saying, though – I thought I could smell smoke. I'd rather you didn't, in the house.'

Silvan smiled enigmatically. 'Part of "sorting him out". Medicinal.'

'Oh, Jesus. Weed? His head's messed up enough as it is at the moment.'

'What? Don't tell me you don't approve? I wouldn't have had you down—'

'No, not normally, of course not. But right now—'

'He seemed happy enough to me with nature's painkiller. Brought a smile to his face and he was sleeping peacefully by the time I left.'

'Maybe, but I'm still not keen.'

'I offered to score some for him.' He looked at her

challengingly. 'He seemed to like the idea. Honestly, it's proven—'

'I know all about the benefits.' She sighed, doubting that Silvan's interest was primarily medicinal. 'I'll talk to him about it. The way I feel right now, I might even join you.'

Silvan laughed. 'Listen, I can imagine how hard it is for you both. If there's anything – anything at all – you need, just give me a shout. I mean it.'

'Thanks. We might well take you up on it.' She looked at her watch. 'But for now—'

'Have you seen Tammy today?'

'Not since last night. I'm not surprised; I know she's still got a lot of revising to do.'

'She texted me. We were supposed to be meeting again tonight but that sour old bitch has grounded her again, it seems. All to impress bloody Northcote, you can bet.'

'That's as may be, but I don't remember going to the pub on a school night myself when I was her age.'

'It was music night. Drinking orange juice, for fuck's sake.'

'She's in the middle of her GCSEs, Silvan. It's important.'

He rolled his eyes. 'Too much bloody pressure these days. Don't you start laying into her as well.'

'It'll be too much pressure if she hasn't done the work she needs to. Show her you care by giving her space. She'll thank you for it in the long run.'

'Bloody hell, Elin, you sound like her mother yourself sometimes.' He waved away her protest. 'I mean it, but in a nice way. You…care about people.' He leaned back with an effortless ease that made the wooden dining chair look like a sumptuous armchair. 'How come you and Bede haven't got kids?'

Elin stared, momentarily speechless.

'You'd make a wonderful mum.' Silvan waved an arm languidly. 'All this the pair of you've got here. It's a kids' paradise.' He frowned and sat up straighter. 'Sorry, hope I haven't put my foot in it. Are you trying?'

She folded her arms.

'If you don't want to talk about it, just say.'

'There's nothing *to* say.' She focused on her exasperation to stop herself from feeling exposed.

'Everything's all right, though, is it? Between you and Bede?'

'For God's sake, Silvan!' She checked herself. Maybe she'd misunderstood, maybe he was simply showing friendly concern. 'Of course we're all right. Apart from the obvious.'

'The obvious?'

'Dealing with the consequences of a serious road accident.'

Silvan nodded. 'He's a lucky man.'

So she hadn't misunderstood.

'Works both ways. I'm lucky to have him, too.' Before he could say anything else, she continued, 'Anyway, what's that you said in your note about being in the shit?'

'Oh, you know Northcote. He—'

A knock on the door startled them both. Elin heard footsteps in the porch and Steve called out. She couldn't remember ever being more pleased to hear his voice.

'Come in.'

He entered, gave her a hug, then looked from one to the other of them in mild surprise. 'Where's the invalid?'

'I know it's early, but he's in bed asleep. Long story. Have you met Silvan?'

'Ah, the one and only. No, but I've heard all about you.' He held out a hand.

'Yeah? How come?' Silvan shook it cautiously.

'I work with Bede. We drove out to a job not long after he'd seen you playing in the pub. Guitar, isn't it? Says you're good.'

'Cheers.' He relaxed back into his kitchen-chair-as-armchair slouch.

'I'm not stopping.' Steve turned back to Elin. 'Just called on my way home to pick up those figures. You got my message, didn't you?'

'They should be in the workshop. I'll go and have a look in a mo.'

Silvan stood abruptly. 'Don't let me keep you. I'll be off.' He looked between her and Steve in a way she didn't like. 'Leave you to it.'

'Sorry, I'll be better company another time. I'm knackered tonight.' Elin handed him the wine bottle. 'Save this for later. Perhaps we can crack it open to celebrate the end of Tamsin's exams, hey?'

'Yeah, perhaps.' He stowed it in his bag, raised a hand in farewell to Steve and turned back to her. 'Pass on my best wishes to the man.'

He gave her another penetrating look and left.

28th May, 2001

Our Bede's got himself a bit of a fan club. Whenever he turns up at Calsthorpe, Tig's eldest, Jack, attaches himself to him. I'd have thought he'd be flattered, but he gets irritated, although he puts a tolerant face on it. He knows what it's like to be the one left out, appreciates what it did for him going down that garage after school and at weekends.

So he's there today, mending Steve's clapped-out old van. I could see him dragging out his patience to give this boy what he'd needed himself. The difference is, young Jack wouldn't know which way up to hold a hammer. He keeps passing Bede the wrong stuff, losing his tools and slowing him down because he doesn't want the kid to hurt himself. And I had to smile because our Bede was at the end of his tether about to send him away once and for all, then Elin walks up and he's suddenly all sweetness and light with the kid and even hands him a screwdriver.

I must give him a pep talk. Or maybe have a quiet word with her. She's obviously interested in him but if he clams up every time she goes near, she'll give up sooner or later. The fact that he's never gone out with a girl (at his age!) was one of the least surprising things he's told me.

Missed my chance for now, though. Had to open my big gob again about the eco-sabotage, didn't I? They've started calling him Engineer and he wears it like a badge of honour. I tried again to tell him to back off a bit. He wasn't so much angry like before, as this deep, sad disappointment.

'I'd have thought you'd have been into it, Joe.'

You could argue with outright anger, but this? I gave up, left early and decided to visit Marjorie before coming home. I've been a few times since we met. She's got this calm, common-sense way of seeing right through a situation. She's also dropped a hint or two about problems with her son Philip in the past – too loyal to say anything outright, but there's a tension there.

Anyway she sympathised about Bede, though I think she wished I hadn't told her about the lawbreaking aspect. Definitely not her scene. Means she's on my side of the argument, though. Didn't come away with any solutions, but at least I'm reassured I was right to confront him.

But that wasn't the big news. I still feel a bit overwhelmed, don't know what I'm going to say to her. She's got this cottage, just out of the village, part of the estate when her family still had an estate, and the old girl who lived there died recently. Marjorie's son and daughter are trying to get her to sell it, but she tells me she doesn't want to. Although I haven't told her the details about me and Suzie, she knows I'm not exactly living in paradise. So – can you believe your bloody luck, Joe Sherwell? – she actually asked did I want to take a tenancy for next to nothing in return for living there and doing the place up?

She took me to see it. Alderleat, it's called. Bloody hell. What estate agents call 'ripe for renovation'. 'Has potential'. Well, it does – on one level I love it, but live there?? I'm wondering how her old dear lasted that long – occupied one room while the rest fell apart around her. I'd say it's doable with a hefty dose of hard work, but of course I'd need some way of making a living. I stopped at the village shop and bought the local paper. There's a builder's merchant a few miles away looking to take someone on. Menial compared to running my own shop, but I've been thinking a lot recently and I'm going to have to sell the business to give Suzie the clean break she's demanding. It slays me to think of selling up after all I put into that shop, but it seems the house isn't enough for her and she's still insisting I stay away from the kids completely. It breaks my heart to lose them, but I'm hardly in a position to argue, am I? Push her too hard and she might start kicking off about the other business.

Maybe I need a clean break, too. Sell the shop, move to Foxover.

Midnight

I was just on my way to bed when the bell went. Our Bede. Said he had to call by, hated the idea of falling out with me. He's not going to change his mind about the sabotage but he'll be extra careful and he's sorry for the way we argued, the things he said. Fair do's.

To be honest I didn't fancy stewing over a row, so instant forgiveness was the order of the day. And besides – I know I probably shouldn't have said anything to him yet about Marjorie's offer, but who else have I got to talk to? (Needless to say I told him nothing about Suzie and selling the business, that's a decision I'll have to make on my own.) He thinks I should go for it. That derelict wreck. Alderleat. He'll come when he can and help me.

Like old times

'Go on, Elin. It'll be like old times.' Fran sounded as though the decision had already been made. 'Do you both the world of good.'

'Me, yes. Both, not so sure.'

Elin stared out of the kitchen window, her friend's voice down the phone competing with the jagged sound of music that drifted through from the living room on a fragrant cloud of cannabis smoke. She'd declined the offer of joining them for a listen to No Surrender's new demo CD, saying she had too much to do. Her pointed look had gone over Bede's head.

'He just hasn't been persuaded properly,' Fran continued. 'Honestly, Elin, I still get asked regularly how the Engineer's doing. He's got an ego like any man's; surely that counts for something. And he needs some practice in case your Northcote gets his wicked way.'

'Please don't tempt fate. I still can't bear to think it might come to that.'

'So join us up here and set a precedent. Put the old misery on to me – I'll tell him what's what.'

The music was spiky and relentless. Elin recognised the song. She was grudgingly impressed, but after what must have been the third repeat, it was beginning to wear a bit thin. She heard the click of backgammon pieces and a burst of stoned laughter.

'Leave it with me, Fran.'

She sighed as she ended the call. They really should go to support the anti-fracking protest. But her energy was at an all-time low and she dreaded Bede refusing point-blank. Now was certainly not the right moment to broach the subject. Silvan's visits had grown ever more frequent – he claimed Philip gave him flexible hours since he worked early mornings, evenings and weekends, but she still suspected a fair amount of skiving. Bede seemed to take more notice of him expounding with the authority of a doctor about the benefits of rest and convalescence than he ever did of Elin's suggestions that doing those jobs he could would not only keep him active but maintain his self-respect. She dreaded a return to the post-Joe depression.

'Who was that?' Bede called through.

She put her head round the living-room door, again declining their invitation to join them and play the winner. 'Fran.'

'She OK? Any news?'

She could be imagining the look he exchanged with Silvan, but it rankled nevertheless. 'I'll tell you about it later. I'll also let you know when Steve calls.'

'Steve?'

'About those plans. The ones he came to pick up days ago, remember?'

'Don't hassle me, love.' His eyes met Silvan's again. This time she definitely didn't imagine it. 'You know I've nearly finished them.'

'"Nearly" won't get the job done. You can't let him down. We need Sunny Days.'

'Thanks for the sympathy. I told you I've had the mother of all headaches today.'

He still suffered momentary blackouts and the migraines that accompanied them. But *the mother of all headaches?* The Silvan-like phrase dampened her sympathy. She walked over to the music centre and turned it down.

'Glad you're enjoying it,' Silvan said.

'I'm not criticising. Actually, I'm looking forward to a proper listen. But it's hardly quiet, soothing, headache-curing stuff, is it?'

As she left the room, she could imagine him mouthing *nag, nag, nag* at her husband. Maybe she was maligning him, but she'd sensed something she couldn't put her finger on ever since that uneasy conversation the evening after he'd rescued Bede from the rain-sodden roadside. She told herself, for Bede's sake, that she was being paranoid. She didn't want to spoil a friendship. Bede needed to be outdoors, always had, and his confinement was grinding him down, making him snappy. The longer it went on, the more she responded in kind. He looked forward to Silvan's visits, especially as he'd refused to go back to the pub since that first time. She only wished she had more time to spend with him herself.

She put on her boots and went out to dig some new potatoes for the shop. Every time she pressed the fork into the ground a tiny bit of tension flowed away through the tines like electricity going to earth. Or like the fluids pumped into the ground to extract the shale gas. Those wouldn't go away, like discharging electricity or relieving her own stress, but would seep into the groundwater and spread, a distorting mirror of the river on the surface, carrying their pollution with them to blight the land. The hovering threat had dimmed a little in her mind as they coped with the aftermath of Bede's accident – if it had been an accident; the police still hadn't identified the joyriders – but Fran's phone call brought it back to the fore. On the whole, she concurred with Bede that since the depressing end to the Calsthorpe Wood protest all those years ago, their best contribution was by deeds rather than words, at

Alderleat. But as Northcote's fracking proposals grew ever more real, and it became increasingly clear that governments and world leaders would continue to ignore the climate crisis, she felt she needed to do something, that there was something they *could* do. The shared purpose might help her and Bede turn another corner. And didn't they have a duty to support Fran's friends? Give and take, solidarity.

At last she heard the front door. Silvan called a cheery goodbye. Elin waved, then watched Bede make his way to the workshop. The wheelchair seemed to be moving in a straight line but she stuck the fork in the ground and went to check. For once, he didn't seem to mind.

'Only one spliff and lots of tea.' He grinned. 'I'll be fine.'

He seemed clear-headed enough and even thought to ask what Fran had said. Elin sat down and told him as he spread the contents of a folder on the desk before him.

'I thought we'd already said we wouldn't be going? You know perfectly well what I think.' He waved away her protest. 'Of course I support their cause. I just prefer to stay home and concentrate on all the useful things we're doing here. Literal "direct action".'

'Isn't that a good reason for going now? When you're less able to do stuff around the place.'

He looked up from his papers. 'You're trying to cram in the physical work of both of us – admirably, I might add – and I'm certainly not going on my own.'

'I'm glad you noticed.' She immediately regretted the sharpness of her tone.

'What's that supposed to mean? Am I not *grateful* enough? I didn't ask for this, Elin.'

'I know, and I sympathise with the shit you're going through. But there's plenty you could be doing.' A pencil dropped to the floor. As he bent to pick it up, she noticed the state of his hair and just managed to prevent herself from commenting about neglecting personal hygiene as well as work. 'Anyway. Fran. It'd only be for a couple of days.'

'Long enough. Another thing, Elin. They can ask after the Engineer all they like but I'm physically incapable of doing anything even if I had the slightest inclination to get involved. Which I haven't. Not any more. They just introduce new laws and injunctions when it suits them. You think I want to run the risk of prosecution and imprisonment? Especially when *they* run no risk at all of anything, bar a paltry delay, for barefaced, unbridled ecocide.'

'Sometimes getting arrested is what's needed – to raise awareness of what's happening, show we mean it.'

'Sorry, but I've had enough of confinement recently, believe me.'

'For goodness' sake! We've got to try, and keep hoping we'll win in the end.'

'Oh, I intend to keep trying. Lobbying the planners – most of the council are on side now – and politicians, unearthing more scientific evidence to throw common sense at them. Working out yet more ways to show it's not economically viable; the only language they understand. Seriously, what's the use of standing at the side of the road with a placard?'

'It lets them know people aren't just going to take it.'

'So they see it and know it, and carry on anyway.'

'Are you going to stand by and let Northcote move in without a fight?'

'Of course not. I am fighting. In ways that don't involve wasting fuel driving all the way up north.'

She rolled her eyes. 'This is bigger than a single car journey. No one's saying we can't go on the bus.' He didn't return her smile. 'Listen, Bede, they'll be supporting *us* when – if – the time comes. The least you could do is turn up. Grey and one or two of the others will be there. It'd be like old times. Fran says they'd love to see you.'

He glared at her. 'Probably so that I – or my wheelchair – can be all over Facebook and in the press. Maybe they want to "raise awareness" by pretending I've been beaten up by some evil capitalist.' The corners of his mouth twitched. 'Oh, sorry, I have been. But that's between me and him. I'm not going to Lancashire, with you, Fran or anyone else. End of.'

'Right.' She took a deep breath. 'I'll go and ring her back.'

She strode to the door.

'Elin.'

She paused, turned.

'You've got a point, love. You know. Around the house and all that. Sorry. I'm a total hermit now till I get these figures finished, promise. If Silvan calls round again I'll tell him I'm busy. You know what, I might even start doing some research for converting a car. Things have moved on in the world of EVs since…you know, since…'

Since he and Joe first considered the idea. She smiled. It wasn't the result she'd hoped for, but she appreciated the peace offering.

The following day, Elin was on duty at the shop. It was quiet for the moment but it had been a hectic morning. She straightened displays and tidied shelves as she waited for Louise to get back from an early lunch. The phone ringing was a welcome distraction from her growing impatience.

'Hello Elin, Brian here.' He sounded unusually hesitant. 'Thought I ought to let you know, there's a woman been in the Horseshoes, kind of asking for you. Well, she was wanting to know about Joe, where he used to live. I knew you were at the shop today and I thought it was better to send her your way – I'm not sure how Bede's fixed at the moment.'

Elin smiled to herself. 'Probably the right call.'

'She seemed a bit of a strange one. Kind of spiky. Just thought I'd warn you.'

No sooner had she put the phone down when the bell over the door rang out and a confident-looking middle-aged woman with a neat blonde bob and smart raincoat walked in and made straight for the counter. Elin forced a smile, surprised at how defensive the newcomer's bearing made her feel.

'Elin Sherwell?'

She nodded.

'I wonder if you can help me. I'm trying to trace Joseph Sherwell. I believe he was living in this village when he died.'

Her northern accent echoed Bede's and Joe's.

'He was. Maybe I can help you – I'm his niece.'

'So the pub landlord said.' The woman frowned. 'I didn't know Joe had a niece.'

'In-law. I'm married to Bede.'

'Who?'

Elin folded her arms. 'I'm sorry, I don't think you introduced yourself.'

'Oh, forgive me. It's all a bit…strange. Suzanne Sherwell.' She held out a hand and Elin shook it. 'Joe's wife. Though I suppose I should say widow – I'm still getting used to the idea.'

Elin let go of her hand as if an electric current had shot through it. 'Joe was married?'

Suzanne Sherwell smiled to herself. 'So that was his game. Pretend we never existed.'

She glanced round as the shop bell rang out and Louise walked in. Elin waved to her, then turned back to her visitor.

'I'm free now. Lunch break.' She indicated the staff room at the back. 'We can talk through there undisturbed.'

The woman sniffed. 'I've got nothing to hide.'

As if Elin had. She bristled as she led the way through to the small rest room.

'Coffee?' she asked as she offered the woman a seat at the table.

'No, thanks; I don't intend to keep you long.' Suzanne Sherwell sat down, hardly waiting for Elin to join her before launching in. 'So, according to Joe, I didn't exist. That explains why you didn't bother to tell me he'd died. I'm surprised your ears haven't been burning. Took me almost two years and a chance encounter with one of his old mates to find out. Mind you, the bastard had been gone a lot longer than that, so I suppose it doesn't make much difference.'

There was no hint of sorrow or loss in her voice. Surely it made some difference to know he was dead, however acrimonious the divorce had been? Acrimonious enough for him to have buried it; hidden it from her and Bede.

'I'm sorry,' she said. 'If we'd known, of course we'd have tried to trace you.'

'There was no mention of us among his things?'

'Us?'

'Me and the kids.'

Elin breathed in sharply. 'No.'

'No will?'

That explained her sudden appearance. 'There was a will, yes.' She felt the woman's eyes boring into her, failing to get past her armour of indignation. 'I was surprised how well-organised his affairs were. He left everything to Bede. They were like father and son.'

'Which is more than he was to Emma and Niall, his own two children.'

'I'm sorry to hear it.'

'Don't give me that; you don't know them from Adam.' She raised her eyebrows. 'Who *is* this Bede, then?'

Elin frowned, beginning to wonder if the woman was who she claimed to be. 'Lydia's son. You knew Lydia? Joe's sister?'

Suzanne looked as smug as a card player about to reveal a winning hand in a game Elin hadn't realised she was playing. 'That would make him a Markham. Not Sherwell.'

Elin held a trump card. 'Lydia married Robert Markham when Bede was seven. They made him take the name for a while, but he reverted to Sherwell when he left home.'

'Oh.' Suzanne's eyes widened. She stared vacantly past Elin. 'So that… I'd assumed she got rid of it,' she murmured.

'Obviously not,' Elin snapped. 'I'm married to it.'

Suzanne appeared to realise what she'd said.

'I'm sorry, I… Thinking aloud. I didn't mean any offence. What…what's your husband told you about his father?'

'Nothing. That his mother refused to talk about him.'

Suzanne relaxed visibly. 'Understandable.'

'So you know?'

'As much as Joe told me.'

'He wouldn't tell us anything.'

'No, if Lydia had decided not to, he probably agreed it was for the best. As do I.'

She bent her head and rummaged in her bag. Elin watched, silently thanking Brian for sending this woman here, not to Alderleat.

'You've said too much now,' she said, her voice catching. 'You've got to tell me what you know.'

'Got to?'

'It's hardly going to make any difference now Joe's dead. As is Lydia.'

'But it makes a difference to me, doesn't it? At the time I was happy to take the house plus a once-and-for-all settlement when he sold the business. It was worth it to see the back of him. Clean break. But that meant he never paid maintenance for the kids. If you get what I mean.'

'I don't know about that,' Elin said, still trying to grasp the situation. 'But there's a legal will. The house was in all three of our names and Joe left his share to us.'

'I don't want a share of some godforsaken place in the middle of nowhere! With other people living in it!'

'He had hardly any savings when he died, either – what he had, he ploughed into...into the smallholding.' She hesitated to reveal the name, even though the woman had got this far and would clearly have no trouble finding it out for herself. She straightened in her seat. 'If you think you have a claim, which I doubt, you should get legal advice. Have you?'

'I've only just found out about Joe. But I certainly will if it comes to it. I thought it might be better to have an amicable chat first. With you and your husband. Can we arrange a meeting?'

'Not yet. Bede took Joe's death badly, and at the moment he's convalescing after a serious accident. I really don't want to burden him with something like this right now. Could you give me a while to tell him in my own way?' She also wanted to see a solicitor before discussing anything.

They sat in silence, regarding one another steadily. After an age, Suzanne cocked her head to one side. 'You seem like an honest girl to me. I've managed this far. But you make sure you talk to your husband before long. I really don't want to have to...'

Her voice trailed off as she opened the notebook she'd removed from her handbag. She jotted down her e-mail address and phone number, tore out the page and placed it on the table between them. To Elin's relief, she stood without asking for anything in return. There was no need; the shop details were no secret.

As Elin escorted her out and watched her leave, she wondered if there could possibly be a right time to tell Bede about this encounter.

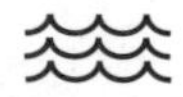

'I've brought you some tea.'

Bede looked up, removed his glasses, smiled. The girl looked as pale as he imagined he did, an apparition of herself.

'Thanks, Tamsin. How are the exams going?'

'Nearly done. They've gone OK, s'pose.' She perched on a thick, gnarled beam; he liked the way she'd begun to make herself at home in the workshop. 'You've been a great help, thanks.'

'Us? You mean keeping an eye on the invalid as an excuse to get out of the house?'

He heard the sarcasm in his own voice as Tamsin reddened.

'It wasn't... Elin's just wanted to make sure someone's on

hand. And I did want somewhere quiet to revise, away from them all.'

That was mean, Sherwell, he thought. Mean and unnecessary. It had been Elin's idea, not Tamsin's, and who could blame Elin for wanting to save him from a repetition of the roadside stranding episode? He appreciated her help, care and concern, he really did; it wasn't her fault that he couldn't come to terms with himself as someone who needed those things.

'But what I really meant,' Tamsin continued before he could apologise, 'was all that stuff you explained. Especially the maths and physics. Felt like it made sense, anyway. We'll see when I get the results.'

'Glad I did some good.' He picked up the mug. 'Good cuppa.'

'Thanks. So, Mr Private Tutor, I thought you were self-taught. How come you know all this GCSE stuff?'

'I never said self-taught. I chose to leave school at sixteen for an apprenticeship. Having done quite well at my exams – especially considering I didn't have an ungrateful bastard next door to watch over so I could get away from the hassle at home.'

She smiled. Apology accepted. 'Though you didn't have Northcote in the house to contend with.'

'Oh, he's a pussycat in comparison. I could write you a book, except English wasn't one of my better subjects. Listen, are you busy? Don't let me keep you.'

'I've got one more exam, end of next week. I'm OK for now, need a break. Elin said to ask if you wanted a hand, actually.'

'Perfect. A hand's exactly what I do want.'

He glanced down at the stained, grubby cast and she laughed.

'I need to distract myself from sheer frustration. I've been doing the calculations and plans for a Sunny Days project and I've been on the internet looking at electric motors and batteries for cars, but it's hardly like being outside. I'm also dying to get back to the caravan – you know Brian came over last week to help Elin get the roof on to protect it from all this rain? I really appreciate it, but I can't be doing with watching from the sidelines – makes me feel useless. So, from the sublime to the ridiculous, I'm trying to make a portable clamping device so I can be a bit more helpful around the house. You know, for chopping veg or, well, anything you need two hands for.'

He showed her the drawings he'd made.

'Looks awesome,' she said. 'You want to patent it.'

'Haven't made it yet. Don't jump the gun.' He twisted a lock of hair round his finger. 'So Bede's Law of Vicious Circles dictates that I'm going to need at least two hands to make it. You know you were asking how the machine tools in here work? I need to shape this block of wood first.' He looked up at the system of bands and gears leading from the water wheel, then at the lathe. 'It's controlled by that lever, see. Have a go, you'll soon get the feel.'

His original intention had been for an extra pair of hands, someone to follow simple instructions, but he was surprised at her initiative, and by how practical and eager to learn she turned out to be. And by the satisfaction he felt from doing something positive.

Elin was right; he'd let things slip. And he realised he'd started taking her and all they had together for granted again.

Restoring some kind of normality

'Cheer up. Anyone would think we'd lost.'

Carole turned to Elin as the last group of customers left the shop.

'Sorry. But it just seems to have brought it home to me that it's not over yet.'

Having drawn the short straw, Carole had held the fort at Foxover Storehouse while the rest of the collective had joined the small crowd at the planning hearing in Shrewsbury. They'd spent most of the day sitting as calmly as they could at the back of the meeting room at the council offices. Bede had refused to carry a placard in the demonstration outside, though Elin had dug out her old Calsthorpe T-shirt in honour of the occasion. Bede had never had one, saying his body art was enough. He'd told her with a smile that he intended to keep his shirt firmly on this time, since there was no point alienating the local worthies. After the argument over Fran's invitation, she was relieved that they could joke about it, and even grateful that he'd turned up at all. Though when he'd challenged Northcote in the corridor – 'See? I'm still here. Didn't work, did it?' – Elin almost wished he'd stayed at home. She was relieved that Philip was too preoccupied to rise to it.

It had been a small victory, but Northcote had announced on the spot that the drilling consortium, Prospect G, would refer it to the Secretary of State.

'I've got no illusions about the thinking at higher levels,'

Elin said, 'and it's going to mean even more research and endless bloody arguing.'

'Nothing like looking on the bright side,' Carole replied as she turned the sign on the door to Closed and locked it. 'You've been cooped up with that cheerful husband of yours for too long.'

'Sorry. Don't get me wrong; I'm glad we've got this far. So's Bede, actually. He's even cooking us a celebratory dinner.'

'You'd better get back to him. I can finish off here. Thanks for bringing the first-hand report. I appreciate it.'

When Elin arrived home, the delicious cooking smells snuggled round her like a fluffy bath towel. Hearing a rattle of washing up, she was momentarily surprised to see someone standing at the sink. As she registered the No Surrender T-shirt and spiky black hair, she realised how much she'd missed Bede's tall figure, his loping gait, and wondered if this was a faint echo of what it must be like to lose someone yet keep on seeing them at unexpected moments. She snapped out of her reverie as Silvan turned with a smile.

'Hi, Elin. Chef's just gone out to set the table. You're dining al fresco tonight.'

'Sounds lovely. What's cooking?'

'Lasagne.' He put a pan to drain and wiped his hands on a towel. 'Don't worry, I'm not stopping.' He looked at her steadily. Once again, she thought of that awkward evening, it must be weeks ago. 'I just called to get the news about today's hearing, and got dragged into helping out with the dishes. He's amazing – I love that veg vice thingy he's rigged up for chopping one-handed – but washing up's obviously a bit awkward and he wanted it all to be done by the time you got back.'

Elin wasn't in the mood for small talk. 'I suppose he's told you how it went.'

'Yeah, great news.'

'Is it? It'll probably turn out to be nothing but a delay, though it was heartwarming to see so many Foxover people there,' she said, her tone letting him know exactly what she thought.

'I wish I could've been with you. But there'd be no point in me losing Philip's trust or my job yet, would there? I couldn't risk being seen with the protesters, and God forbid he should think I was there to support him.'

She nodded, saved from further comment by the familiar electric whirr that announced Bede's approach.

'Don't tell me Silvan's claimed all the credit for my culinary efforts.'

'Not at all.' Elin smiled and stooped to kiss him. 'You've been busy,' she said, eager to talk about something other than the day's events. 'Smells delicious. Have I time for a quick shower?'

'See you out in the garden when you're ready,' he said. 'I thought we'd take the rare opportunity of a sunny evening to eat outside.'

When she returned, she felt a flash of irritation on hearing Silvan's voice. Hadn't he gone yet? In the kitchen, Bede was awkwardly ladling a portion of the lasagne into a pot, which he covered and handed over.

'Cheers, mate.' Silvan looked at Elin. 'I was just waiting for you to get back so I could say my fond farewells. I'll leave you to it.'

Elin shook her head after him as he left.

'Are we turning into a soup kitchen?' she asked sharply.

'He was more or less inviting himself to stay and eat with us. It was the kindest way I could think of to ease him out of the door. I know you don't like him much.'

'I wouldn't go that far.'

'He's been really good company recently, while you've been busy doing the work of two of us. He's kept me sane sometimes, to be honest.'

She decided it was safest not to comment further. Not when he was making such an effort. The table in the sheltered garden looked inviting, with salad, bread and wine glasses. He'd even brought napkins, a rarity if not a first. The setting was idyllic. The murmuring of the stream harmonised with the deeper trickle of water through the cracks in the leat's sluice gate – a perfect soundtrack to the view in the warmth of the setting sun.

As they ate, she thought beyond the hearing and all it represented, even daring to wonder if Bede turning out meant her worries about his growing insularity were unfounded. He'd hardly gone anywhere for a long time. They'd been for a couple of walks together, but his heart hadn't been in it and he hadn't ventured beyond Alderleat on his own since Silvan had found him in the rain. She'd given up even suggesting they went to the Horseshoes in the evenings. He had his next check-up appointment in a couple of days and they anticipated he'd be relieved of the cast on his arm. She hoped that would be the start of restoring some kind of normality, and maybe she'd even find the right moment to break the news of Suzanne Sherwell to him.

His eyes sparked as he talked about the planning victory, reflecting the fiery golden highlights the sun lent to his hair. She realised she'd been missing his vitality and determination as much as the sight of him on his feet.

She laid her fork to rest on her empty plate and, remembering Carole's admonition, tried to summon up her own enthusiasm. She felt weary, as though coping with the last few weeks had sapped her ability to enjoy the moment.

Bede squeezed her hand and she looked at him, felt the flicker of a smile she didn't have the energy to hold on to.

'Come here,' he said.

She drew up her chair to his side. Despite the physical awkwardness, she'd never felt so comforted by the steady calm of his embrace. She clung to him, buried her face in his chest and let go the flood of tears she'd been damming up for days, weeks, months. He rocked her gently; she felt his warm breath in her hair. She loved him for not speaking, for simply holding her and allowing her what she so rarely allowed herself: to let go.

She cried herself dry, then drew away and looked into his eyes. He wiped her cheeks, one at a time, with one of the unaccustomed napkins. She took it and finished the job, without taking her eyes off him. He ran his hand through her hair as he kissed her.

'You needed that,' he said softly.

'I need you,' she said, getting up and leading the way inside.

On the way home from the hospital, Bede flexed his left arm, opening and closing his fingers and revelling in the freedom of movement. It looked pale and sickly, felt weak, but that would pass. His ankle would take longer; he'd known that, but it was a smaller, lighter cast and he felt freedom within his grasp.

Elin glanced briefly at him before turning her eyes back to the road. 'I'm hiding those crutches upstairs.'

She had a point. Despite the advice not to put weight on his wrist too soon, he probably would be tempted to use them and risk putting himself back to square one.

'Do you want to stop off somewhere on the way back?' she asked.

'Not really. Let's get home.'

'You sure?' She glanced at him again.

He shrugged. 'Where did you have in mind?'

'I was thinking of you,' she said. 'You're the one's been staring at the same four walls for weeks.'

There was a fragility to her voice. The endless rounds of phone calls, e-mails and social media posts after last week's hearing must be getting to her.

'Honestly, no need to worry about me,' he said. 'Now I've got my hand free, I'll be able to work on the caravan again. Can't wait to get stuck in.'

'Apart from the fracking hearing, you haven't been anywhere for ages.'

He turned and stared at her. 'What's the big deal? I haven't been particularly mobile, in case you hadn't noticed.'

'Don't get sarcastic.'

'I hope you don't think…there's anything more to it than that.'

'What makes you say that?' She still had that brittle edge to her voice.

'Same thing as makes you turn staying at home for a while into an accusation.'

She sighed. He was relieved to get back to Alderleat, the sun shining in welcome. Having his arm free meant that it was easier to manoeuvre out of the car and into the wheelchair, and he felt life was beginning to look up.

He suggested they make the most of the nice weather and, as they'd taken to doing, they went to sit out on the terrace by the mill stream. While Elin went indoors to make tea, he braced himself gingerly on the arms of the wheelchair, feeling a slight, possibly imagined tug at the point of the healed fracture. He levered himself up and hopped a couple of steps to sit on the garden bench. Elin came out and sank down beside him. As he placed his left arm around her and hugged her to him, the sense of reborn equality was intoxicating.

She raised a hand to his, encircling his fingers loosely in a kind of reunion. They sat for a few moments watching the water in the leat flicker past.

'I've been meaning to tell you,' Bede said. 'You know when Silvan was here yesterday?'

'Reality calling.' She sighed. 'What – did he finally give you some nugget of inside info on Northcote's appeal?'

Bede laughed briefly. 'He's hardly lived up to that promise, has he? No, the opposite. He's been given his notice.'

Officially, Northcote said he was over-staffed, but Silvan was convinced his employer had become suspicious of his growing friendship with Bede and Elin.

'I suppose I sympathise.' She stroked the soft V between his thumb and forefinger as if sending healing waves through the skin.

'It's not just his job,' Bede said. 'He lives in the keepers' accommodation in the village, doesn't he? He'll have to move out and he…he was wondering if we could help out. You know, let him crash at ours for a while, maybe put in a word for him at the Storehouse. Or even find some work for him with us – not paid, but, you know, pitching in for food and lodging.'

'No way!' He'd been sensing a growing atmosphere between them, but her vehemence surprised him. 'I'm sorry, but he's far too unreliable – for us, let alone to recommend to the shop collective. He's done enough skiving that we know of. I wouldn't wish it on him, but I'm not surprised he's got the sack. I bet Northcote's been waiting for an excuse.'

He had to admit she had a point. 'What about putting him up for a bit, though?'

'You're joking. He'd suffocate us.'

'We were all right with communal living at Calsthorpe.'

'That was never our permanent home. We stayed there for periods at a time.'

'Until we got married and moved in with Joe.' He'd sometimes sensed her desire for their own space – one of the reasons he'd found it hard to open up to her about grieving, but now a possible way of talking her round.

'There's no comparison. Joe was family. *And* he had a decent sense of personal space.' That surprised him. 'Whereas Silvan…'

Her reaction was stronger than he'd feared. 'He needn't be in the house. He suggested he'd help us finish the caravan, then maybe… You know… It's stood there sad and unfinished for weeks now, and it'd be a way—'

'That's supposed to be for visitors – income, Bede – and for us. You said he could *live there*?'

'No, I said I'd have to ask you first.'

'First? Jesus, that implies there's a "second". That it might happen.'

'What was I supposed to say? I thought it'd give me – us – time to think.'

'The chance to make it all my fault when we refuse.'

'Don't be daft.'

'I mean it. He seems to have this image of me as a nagging "'er indoors". Don't try and deny it. I'm sure he even thinks I'm siding with Kate to turn Tamsin against him.'

He was almost glad they were having this conversation;

she obviously needed the release valve. 'You're overreacting, love.'

'Maybe it's something to do with the lack of support I get from you.'

His first reaction was to defend himself, but her expression made him pause.

'I thought things were getting better,' she continued. 'I understand what you've been through and it's been heartwarming to see you wanting to do things again. But whenever he's here you simply don't get off your arse. Like yesterday, I'm out at the shop and the Fields till late and I get home to find you couldn't even heat a pan of chili. I'd left it all ready; you knew what time I'd be back. Not much to ask, was it? You should've seen the contempt on both your faces when I mentioned it.'

'I never—'

'"Hey, hey, chill, woman. Give the guy a break. He's still convalescing." And you, sitting there trying not to laugh.'

'I didn't mean…'

She sighed. 'I'm sure you didn't. You're just not yourself when you're with him.'

He folded his arms, trying his damnedest not to feel guilty, but failing miserably. 'Is that what you think?'

'I don't think, I see.'

She turned away from him, staring into the ripples of the leat, her eyes bright. The welling tears pierced him. *I thought things were getting better.* So had he. And they were. He refused to admit he was that easily led – he'd never mock or criticise her like that – but if it was the impression she was getting, he was prepared to concede. For her sake. For both their sakes.

Once again he enclosed her fingers with his newly liberated hand.

'Don't worry, I'll tell him,' he said.

Her smile was like the sun after a storm. He had no idea what he was going to say, but if he and Elin needed time together, he'd do anything to make sure they got it.

The escapism of believing

'I'm off to the caravan to do some plank-nailing,' Elin said.

'Nice word, that: planknailing.' Bede had to say something to stop the wrong words escaping: yes, we agreed, but please stay, give me some moral support…

'Do you want a hand?' Silvan had arrived as if on cue shortly after they finished their dinner.

'I'm fine, thanks,' Elin said. 'I think my good man wants a word with you in any case.'

The good man shot her an imploring look. 'Don't you—?'

'See you later, guys.'

She waggled her fingers and slipped her feet into her boots. He noticed the laces flapping and imagined her getting a safe distance across the yard before stopping to tie them. Kip followed her out.

Thanks, mate, he sent out to the dog. You're on your own, Sherwell.

He told himself he was making a mountain out of a molehill. Silvan would probably just laugh it off, pack his stuff and head off back to Birmingham or Oswestry or wherever it was he'd come from. But no. Bede was pretty sure it wouldn't be so easy. Why feel bad about it? He wasn't their personal responsibility. Tamsin wouldn't like it if he had to leave, but that wasn't their problem, either.

He looked up. Silvan caught his eye, waiting. As if he knew every thought that was going through Bede's mind.

'Fancy a beer?' Bede said. Why? Why say that?

'Is there something to celebrate?'

Bede raised his left hand like a trophy. 'It'll be a while yet before I'm arm-wrestling, but you could say part-way to freedom.'

Or you could call it vulnerable. Like a snail without its shell.

Silvan waved away his attempt to get to his feet, fetched two bottles of Elin's beer from the crate, glasses from the cupboard and poured. He savoured the first mouthful. 'Is she as good at putting a wall together as she is at brewing this?'

Bede nodded as he tried to think how to begin.

'Message received and understood,' Silvan said.

'What message?'

'Here's to the happy little nuclear family.' He raised his glass, waited for Bede to pick his up and when he didn't, clinked the untouched glass where it sat. 'Though I suppose being anti-nuclear goes with the territory.' He laughed briefly.

'I said, what message? What territory?'

Narrowed eyes regarded him steadily: you know perfectly well on both counts. And I know that you know… Layers of knowing like the infinity of mutually reflecting mirrors.

'The territory of a certain set of ideals,' Silvan said. 'But literally, too. Territorial. Not that I blame you. People are. Forgive me for assuming you were different. You know, for a while, I even thought she was different. "Sharing a set of ideals makes us all part of one big family…"'

He'd caught her Welsh accent perfectly, but Bede didn't recall either of them saying anything of the sort.

'I get it,' Silvan continued. 'I get why you let her stalk off when she's obviously knackered and carpentry's the last thing she wants to be doing. To prove you don't need my help. No help, no digs. Yeah, I'll save you the trouble: message understood.'

He picked up his glass and drank. Bede watched, unwilling to admit Silvan was right, unable to put into words how he felt.

'So, come on, why do you find it so difficult to say "sorry mate, no can do"? Does the thought of refusing a friend in need make you feel uncomfortable?' He ticked off a finger. 'No need to worry. I'm not really in need.' He leaned forward. 'Is it because you're torn between what you'd have done yourself and pleasing her?' Another finger folded down. 'A word of advice: open your eyes, stand your ground.'

Silvan's eyes came to rest on a sheet of Sunny Days headed paper lying on the pile of envelopes on the table. Bede noticed how a splash of beer had stained it.

'But I can see why you keep putting her first. I understand here,' Silvan tapped his head, 'and one day I may know from experience what it's like to be that much in love.' Staring at Bede, he flicked all his fingers open. 'No, I think the main reason you find it hard to refuse me is because it makes you realise you're just the same as anyone else. You're not different. Saving the world – your little part of it – doesn't make you special. Oh, we all need to work together, see the bigger picture, refuse to be blinded by individual greed – until it comes to our own little space. And that's the one I can't help you with, Bede. You'll have to work it out for yourself.'

He got up slowly, went over to the crate and returned with another bottle. Looking steadily at Bede's still untouched glass, he removed the crown cork with a tiny fizz and drank straight from the bottle, stirring up sediment to cloud the beer. Bede felt like smashing it from his hand.

'Go on, say something. Unleash the legendary Sherwell anger.'

Bede folded his arms across his chest. It felt good to be able to.

'Thanks for the psych session,' he said with deliberate calm. 'You know what? I can't be arsed arguing with you. I'll just leave it at thanking you for making this easy.' He half-smiled. 'I was dithering, you know. Yes, Bede Sherwell does sometimes dither. When you came in just now, I was almost hooked by that air of who-cares, letting-go, that you do so well. It's buoyed me up recently and I like it, I won't deny it. So there I was, questioning our decision. Almost beginning to wonder how – if it came to it – how to tell Elin I'd relented and you'd be moving in after all. But you've saved me the trouble. Thanks.'

Their eyes met. He could read nothing in Silvan's.

'Tell me one thing before you go.' He placed a subtle emphasis on *go.* 'What's all this about? You cheered me up when I was stuck in the house, but I can't help feeling you don't particularly like us. Looking back, I've caught the occasional whiff of antagonism from the moment we met. So come on, why've you been hanging round this achingly normal, deluded pair of smug bastards? Why want to fucking move in with them?'

Silvan drained the bottle, then slowly rose to his feet. Without taking his eyes from Bede's, he walked to the door, put the bottle in the empties crate and paused, hand on the latch.

'You really have no idea, have you?'

The moment he left, Bede picked up his beer glass and drained it, a trickle escaping, dribbling past his chin to the shirt he'd put on clean for the hospital appointment that morning. He brushed at the stain in irritation. No idea! What idea did he have? Did he know what it was like to find a home, a woman you loved to the ends of the earth, a place to feel secure? Somewhere you could withdraw from battles and guilt and just live life the way you thought was right, immersed in nature, away from the destructions of the twenty-first century world. Not selfish. Didn't everyone need their space?

He looked up at a movement through the window pane. Hadn't he gone yet? Elin was coming back from the caravan. She'd soon give Silvan short shrift and they could be alone to talk it through. The argument had unsettled him more than he cared to admit and he needed to put his mind at rest.

Bede turned to the table and lined up the glasses and bottles. He neatened the pile of bills, removing the stained, wasted Sunny Days paper to rip in half as a scribble sheet for the phone. *Open your eyes.* He closed them, saw the scene at this very table. Wasn't it the night Northcote's car had been scratched? All that fuss. But had it really been enough fuss to drive away the memory of an awkward falling-silent, a brief conspiratorial glance, the slight flush of a cheek? Only to resurface now, so long after the event that he could be imagining it.

Through the window he saw Elin cross the yard. Talking to Silvan, standing too close. A furtive glance toward the house. On the opposite wall, he noticed how the glass of the picture frame superimposed the image of the window onto their wedding photo, a reflected shadow of himself, now, in between. Layers of knowing. *You really have no idea, have you?*

Elin removed her drizzle-damp sweatshirt together with the lingering tingle of the unwanted hug. 'Music Night on

Wednesday? Perhaps we can play together one last time.' As if they were close friends about to part forever. Bloody drama queen. She called to Bede and went upstairs to get a dry jumper.

'Fair-weather DIYer,' he said with a smile on her return. 'You didn't last long.'

She flopped down beside him, rested her head on his shoulder.

'To be honest, Bede, I didn't get started. I was shattered. I sorted through the materials, then found myself just looking at it all, energy sapped. I hope you don't think I'm a hypocrite.'

He ran his hand over her hair and rested it on her shoulder.

'I don't think anything. We'll get it done. When we're ready.'

'So, what did he say?' She sensed him draw back slightly. After Silvan's hushed comments about Bede behaving strangely, she wondered what to expect.

'Oh, he wasn't exactly thrilled. It was a conversation I'd rather not have had.'

'I wonder if he'll move away? It'd be a shame to lose touch completely.'

He looked at her, expression unreadable. 'Would it?'

'Well…maybe not.' She slouched against him and closed her eyes. She'd had more than enough of Silvan for one evening. 'Fran called today.'

'Oh?'

'Said she was pleased about the outcome of our hearing. As cynical as we are about the next stage.' Elin sat up straight. 'Listen, Bede, she asked again whether we'd go and give them our support.'

'Support? We've sent them all the research we've found

– all that's not specific to our local area. I've written letters and signed petitions till my fingers hurt. You told her last time that we weren't going.'

'She wondered if I'd managed to persuade you.'

Bede sighed, rolled his eyes. 'Haven't we been talking about keeping some time and space for ourselves?'

'It would be a few days. Hardly the same as getting a full-time lodger.' He remained impassive. 'Won't you—'

'Come off it,' he snapped, the harshness of his voice causing Kip to look up. 'We've talked about this one often enough. Whether it's Lancashire or even our own doorstep, you know what I feel, deep down. Saving the world? Really? Think we can?'

She was taken aback by his anger. 'Of course I—'

'It's the human race needs saving! The world will keep turning long after we've pushed ourselves to extinction!'

Elin watched him wind a strand of hair round and round his wrist, as if calling the familiar gesture into play to replace the cast, hide any weakness. He upset her when he talked like this.

'Sorry,' he said and she realised she was shaking her head, unsure if she was disturbed by his cynicism or the creeping admission that he had a point. 'Why not enjoy the escapism of believing it for a while? Surround yourself with like-minded people. Warm. Family. Spiritual, even. Don't get me wrong, El. That sense of community. It's good. But let's not delude ourselves – that's what it's about. It's not actually going to change anything. Occasionally a road's delayed, a factory cleans up its act for a while, plans for test drilling get frustrated. But nothing much changes in the wider picture.'

'We've shown that we can win. Every victory means something. Sooner or later—'

'Little victories, yes. They're what make it all worthwhile. But vast swathes of forest continue to be destroyed – every day! Fossil fuels continue to churn up the atmosphere and deposit layers of crap in the oceans while floating continents of plastics wash at the shores. The tipping point gets closer every day and you've still got the Northcotes of this world pretending it isn't happening, because it suits their consumerist growth economy. Little victories help us to cope with all that, but they don't change enough!'

His hand paused in its circling, tense, as though he were about to yank his own hair out.

'Bloody hell, Bede. Whatever happened to the Engineer?'

He laughed harshly. 'I rest my case. Calsthorpe Wood died, remember? Its heart lies buried under tarmac, and the rest can't breathe for noise and fumes. Tell me how we saved *that*.'

'Surely you can't be saying we should just give in and do nothing.'

'Nothing? *Nothing?* Call me selfish, people do, but I'd say we've got our own "little victory": Alderleat. I thought you agreed.'

'Yes, but—'

'And…and if that's not enough, if it really is too bloody selfish, at least we're getting people fixed up with renewable energy through Sunny Days. With Steve.' Something about the way his eyes fixed on hers made her feel uneasy. After a moment, something seemed to give and he looked away. 'But if every now and then you need that sense of family you feel you don't get from me – that elusive dream – I understand. There's nothing to stop you going with Fran.'

'But—'

'I'm fine. Safe to leave on my own. Capable of looking after myself.'

'Without anyone *fussing* over you.'

He was testing her, especially with his digs about family. She had no energy for the game. What had happened to the intimacy that had resurfaced recently? Was that what it had been, intimacy? Or simply a chance for him to prove that the weakness of the last few weeks was receding: 'Not only am I no longer dependent, but I can comfort and protect you, too.' They'd made love with all the passion of their early days. Or had she imagined it, wanted to believe?

'I've had an idea, Elin.' Cold, detached. It wasn't going to be an idea she liked. 'Why don't you ring Steve, ask him whether he's lost his passion…for activism?'

'What?' She felt trapped by the emphasis of his words. 'What's Steve got to do with anything?'

'You want someone to go with you. I'm not up for it; I'm just saying he's someone who might be.' He leaned forward, eyes boring into her. 'Is there something else he's been up for recently, Elin?'

'Keeping the projects going while you've been unwell. Visiting you to see how you are.'

'Visiting *you* when I'm not so alert and wakeful?'

'No, Bede.'

'So why did you blush like a teenager when I mentioned him? Why did I come home that night he first appeared back on the scene to find you both looking so furtive? Why does Silvan of all people seem to think something's going on? Show me some respect, Elin.'

She'd always feared this moment, deep down, but now it was here, it caught her off guard. She struggled for a reply. 'I have no idea what Silvan's been saying. He's got no grounds whatsoever for thinking anything.'

He folded his arms. 'Now if that were me, the first thing I'd do would be to deny it. Not to bang on about what Silvan thinks. Is that because you can't deny it?'

'Bede.'

She reached out to touch him, to release his tightly folded arms. He edged away.

'Go on, deny it.'

'I...' Beneath the anger and provocation she saw hurt. 'There's nothing going on between me and Steve.'

'Nicely worded. Now tell me there never has been.'

However much she wanted to, she couldn't lie to him. 'I'm sorry, Bede. I can't deny once. It was more than a year ago. It only happened once.'

She couldn't look at him.

'"It happened." Like you had nothing to do with it.'

'You'd vanished up north. I was feeling so alone and lost. He was just there. I can't tell you how sorry I am. All it did was make me feel guilty as hell and prove how much I love you at a time when, I'll confess, I was finding you incredibly difficult to live with. So you could almost say it was a good thing.'

He gave a snort of derision. '*You* could, maybe. Happen I couldn't. I don't see how my wife shagging my friend behind my back could ever be a "good thing". And since you chose not to come clean, to lie to me with silence, how can I ever believe it was only once? You've fancied him ever since Calsthorpe.'

'You're kidding, aren't you? There's no—'

'I always thought there was nothing in it because... well...us. But now...' He shook his head. 'Anyway, why have you been so eager to get me out of the house? Why are you suddenly so weird about Silvan? Guilty conscience, perhaps?'

'Oh come on, Bede! I can't believe you said that.'

'Maybe because – oh, forget it.' He put his palms to his eyes and bowed his head. 'You'd better go to Fran's. Give us both time to think.'

‘You can forget bloody Silvan, all right?’ He stared at the floor in silence. ‘Won’t you even look at me? Try and talk?’

She reached out again.

‘Get off me!’ He shoved her away roughly. ‘Just go.’

She stood and slowly made for the stairs, fighting tears as she said his name one more time. He refused to look at her.

‘I’m going to pack.’

She waited for him to call her back. She tiptoed around the bedroom, opening cupboards and drawers quietly so she wouldn’t miss the sound of his voice, hesitating every time a floorboard creaked even though she knew she’d hear him above it. When the whirr of the wheelchair was followed by the familiar clicks and quiet thud of the door opening and shutting, she picked up the phone to call Fran. She put it down before she’d finished dialling. Not yet; there was still a chance…she hadn’t left yet.

Leaning on the old timbers of the footbridge, loving the age combined with the knowledge they’d been restored by his own hands and those of the two people he loved, Bede gazed down into the mill stream and unfocused his eyes to make a braid of the water; a long, sparkling braid that tumbled over a beloved shoulder.

Tell your big sister I’ll be down to see her as soon as I can. I’ve missed her.

His silent words were taken up and borne down to the river.

Talking to the water again?

He kept his eyes focused-unfocused on the rippling beauty of the leat.

Doesn't come back at you with feelings of its own, does it?

Bede tried to tune in to the voice of the leat, the bubbling chatter against the background hushing torrent, a language of familiar sounds but a meaning he had not quite learnt to penetrate.

You should try talking to the one who matters.

If he turned his head, he'd see. If he reached out, he'd feel. He heard a click and above the green algal smell of the sluice gate, caught a hint of Joe's cigarette smoke.

I'm not surprised, you know. When did you last tell her you love her?

All the time.

Actually tell her?

Shrug. Last night.

Last night? You held her. That was nice. You fucked her.

We made love.

If you never let her know how much she means to you, you fucked.

He refused to turn and look. She knows. We made love. Fucking's what she does with other people.

Once, she said. Can't you let it go?

What about the others? I should have seen it before now.

You sure about that?

I'm not sure about anything.

Talk to her. Go with her tomorrow. Sort it out.

He stared at the strong timbers, at the shiny greased twin ratchets, at his own hands resting on the rail. Stared at the braided current, the white noise of the overflow filling his head until the light began to fade and the air smelled mossy green, watery clear, and all trace of cigarette smoke was gone.

Only then did he dare glance at the space to the side of his elbow.

Wishful thinking. It's all wishful thinking.

As Elin carried her bag out to the car, the movement of the dog nosing around the edge of the yard caught her eye. She looked across and saw Bede leaning on the rail of the little footbridge over the leat, the wheelchair abandoned before the step up to it. The sight of him tugged at her heart and she called out to him, despite herself. He didn't move. A slight breeze played at his hair, and the evening light caught the spray from the stream in a translucent haze to the side of him.

She called once more, then got into the car, slammed the driver's door and started up. The thought of leaving now filled her with unease. She revved the engine noisily.

Still, he didn't turn.

When Bede got back to the house, it was in darkness. Before he could think about whether to call up the stairs, he saw Elin's note on the kitchen table. He hated the stream, its seductive voice with layers of meaning just out of reach, for siren-calling him with shades of Joe, long and loud enough to drown the sound of the car. Letting her go, taking the moment for talking with her.

Everywhere's under threat

'Great! So what did you say to persuade Misery Guts to take up his bed and walk?'

'I didn't. I left him to lie in it.'

'Whoa. That was said with feeling. I can see a late night ahead while you tell Aunty Fran all about it.'

'It's doing me good already just to be away. I'll see you later.'

Elin cut the call and stared through the windscreen at the passing headlights. Every so often the car rocked as a lorry whooshed past the layby. She felt similarly shaken. She wasn't proud of herself. Maybe she should have found the right moment to come clean to him before – but when was the right time for a conversation like that? Maybe she should have refused to be drawn. But she couldn't lie to him. However hurt he was, the depth of his rejection shocked her. She'd come back to him, chosen him, stuck by him, however difficult he'd been. Didn't she have her limits, too? His stubborn refusal to come with her rankled. She hated his negativity, although a nagging voice told her his views were nothing new, they weren't so far from her own, and she was only seeing it as negativity because of the stress they'd been under. She suppressed the urge to phone home. He'd said time apart would give them both time to think. He was right about that, at least.

Blinking away tears, she sat for a moment, gathering herself, before picking up the phone again.

'What have you said to him, Steve?'

'I haven't said a thing. Are you OK? You know you'd be welcome here if you're stuck. I can't believe he chucked you out.'

'Don't over-dramatise. I was thinking of going to Fran's for a few days anyway. Do you really think I'd come to yours after all this?'

'What do you take me for? It'd be perfectly innocent.'

'Try telling Bede that.'

'I'm not up for trying to tell Bede anything.'

She smiled grimly to herself. 'Even so. Aren't you supposed to be meeting up to discuss business in the next few days – now he's more mobile? Please can you use it as an excuse to try and talk to him?'

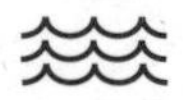

As Elin and Fran walked over to join the crowd of protesters, she imagined the fields beyond Holtwood similarly fenced off and turned into a cold, ugly industrial site. The reality of this scene caused a surge of anger to well up inside her. The local protesters had been joined by a number of seasoned campaigners from various walks of life, and she recognised with a wave of nostalgia the grizzled beard and shaven head of Grey, the homely figure of Tig by his side.

'You were right about old faces,' she said to Fran. 'A real blast from the past.'

Warmth flowed through her as their friends' faces lit up in recognition.

'See?' Fran said quietly as they approached. 'The break from routine's doing you good already.'

'Break from routine and over a hundred miles' distance.'

'Things still looking that bad in the cold light of day?'

Were they? It had done her good to unburden herself, talking to Fran until the small hours of the morning, like old times. Yet, ironically, the more her friend comforted, soothed, supported her point of view, the more she leapt instinctively to Bede's defence. She still had no idea what to think.

Putting it behind her, she lost herself to the moment, relishing the warm hugs and whoops of joy at the reunion. Had it really been fourteen years since the demise of Calsthorpe Wood? The mood turned more sombre as they talked about Joe. It was the first time she'd seen them since his death and they seemed genuinely sorry that he'd left the community under such a cloud. Grey's eyes twinkled as he asked after Bede; another cloud that seemed to have lifted during the years of absence. Elin wished once again that he'd come. She told them about the accident, loyally omitting to mention his opinion of protests such as this one.

A murmur rippled through the crowd as the first vehicles approached the site. They raised their banners and their voices as though their passion really could halt the inevitable progress of the contractors. She could have been back at Calsthorpe. History repeating itself as they faced an endless cycle of wanton destruction. Interspersed with the encouraging hoots of support from passing cars, she heard several cries of 'Get a job!' Apart from their pathetic inability to come up with a more rational argument, what made them think she didn't have one?

As she yelled out her anger and frustration, fuelled by all the emotion of the recent months, Elin silently thanked Bede for inspiring her, if not in the way she would have wanted. By the time the high-vis jackets of the police and security guards closed in, she realised her face was wet with tears. Brushing them away with the back of her hand, Elin flashed a smile from Fran to Tig, fervently hoping no one would mistake it for cowardice.

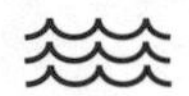

Bruised and shaken from being roughly manhandled out of the way, they watched from a distance as the gates to the site closed and an unease descended like the calm before a storm. Elin's cheeks were still glowing in defiance. She looked up to see a reporter, followed by a cameraman and the furry squirrel of an outside broadcast mike.

'Emotions are clearly running high.' Huddled in a down jacket against the stiff breeze, the young woman turned to her. 'Do you mind if I have a word?'

Elin glanced at Fran, who exchanged looks with the others and edged her forward. 'A new face,' she whispered. 'Add some weight. Show the world it's not a case of nimbyism.'

Smiling with a courage she didn't feel, Elin steeled herself and nodded to the reporter.

'I understand you've come a long way to lend your support to the people here.'

'From Shropshire. The Welsh border. No distance is too far to try and put a stop to this madness.'

'I'm sure they're glad of the solidarity. Is your area under threat from fracking, too?'

'I'm afraid so. They haven't been given the go-ahead yet, and we'll do our best to make sure they don't. It's highly unlikely that the geology's right, if…if nothing else.' She paused, the emotion of the day and the last few weeks catching up with her, as her friends nearby voiced noisy encouragement. 'But in truth,' she continued, 'everywhere's under threat.'

'Under threat. But the consortium assures us the risks are minimal and everything's carefully controlled. That your group's talk of pollution and earth tremors is scaremongering. What do you say to that?'

Elin shook her head, finding it uncharacteristically hard to stay calm. 'Of course those with vested interests would say that. I'm an environmental science graduate and I can tell you those risks are very real, but that's by no means all. It's such short-termism! Here they are, prospecting for a new source of fossil fuels at a time when we desperately need to be cutting out their use – for the sake of the climate, the world and us all!'

Fran beamed at her from behind the small film crew. Elin fought the irrational tears as she went on to praise the efforts of the local protesters over the months and years.

'You were magnificent,' Tig whispered as the camera stopped rolling and the sound guy lowered the mike.

The young reporter asked if she'd wait a few moments. 'I just want to interview a representative of the consortium.' She waved her hand at a car that had been slowly edging its way through the gathered protesters. 'Then I'd like to give you the last word.'

Elin looked across. The tinted window slid down and she locked eyes with the man who was scowling at her from the safety of the passenger seat.

'You,' Philip Northcote said as Elin marched over to the car. 'What on earth are you doing here?'

'I could ask you the very same thing.'

He waved angrily at someone behind her, and she realised the small film crew were following her, the reporter explaining to viewers that they were about to speak to a member of the drilling consortium. She asked if Elin knew Mr Northcote. Ignoring both the question and the anger

Philip radiated, Elin leaned on the car, halting its creeping progress.

'Do you honestly not realise what you're doing?' Again she struggled to keep her voice steady. She waved at the ugly drilling rig towering into the sky, the sturdy fences and concrete service roads, then held up the placard she and Fran had been carrying, showing before and after photos of this scene and a tranquil field. 'Isn't it enough for you?' She turned to the camera. 'This man is not only looking to make a fast buck by desecrating the earth *here*, but he wants to do it again, and again. Just to make absolutely certain the effects are felt by us all.'

The car window was sliding up, but she reached out and gripped the top of the pane, cringing as she forced him to stop.

'Don't get hysterical,' he muttered as if to a child. 'Let go and stop making a fool of yourself.'

'He's also providing land in the *village where he lives* for another monstrosity like this! Of course, he can move away if it turns out badly. I dare say he can pay whatever it takes to survive the effects of climate crisis and ecocide. But not forever. What sort of world will it be?' Elin leaned towards the crack in the window. 'Even animals don't shit in their own burrows!'

She hardly felt the burly security guard drag her away from the car, didn't hear what the reporter was saying, immersing herself instead in the supportive huddle of her friends. She felt light-headed as they stood in the growing drizzle, fully aware that Northcote would shake off her words just as the windscreen wipers cleared the rain.

This is no fun

Tamsin tried Silvan's phone again. Straight to voicemail. She left a brief message. Here she was, her exams over, supposed to be making the most of these last few days before she went on holiday with her dad and kid brother, and he'd done a vanishing act on her. Perhaps he was next door, though he usually texted her when he was going to Alderleat so they could 'accidentally' meet there, save her the inevitable argument with her mum. If he wasn't there, maybe Elin or Bede would know where he was. A visit was overdue in any case; she liked helping Bede out in the workshop, the way he didn't patronise her, and she always felt better after talking to Elin.

As she crossed the yard, Kip came bounding up to her. She fussed him, looked around, popped her head into the greenhouse, tried the workshop door and found it locked. It was unusual for the dog to be running around unsupervised. Before she could grab his collar, he ran off into the bushes between the yard and the field beyond.

At the house, no one answered her knock. She tried the door; it opened. Her hopeful 'Hello?' faltered. It looked different. Smelled different – stale food and drink hanging in the air. Among a scattering of the papers that usually sat in a neat pile on the edge of the kitchen table, a dirty plate had been left with a smeared glass placed precisely in the centre. A few more and a stack of encrusted pans lay more haphazardly next to the sink. The vase of flowers Elin always had on the table were wilted and discoloured. Weird.

Whatever was going on in their lives, the place always seemed tidy – something Tamsin liked to mention whenever her mum started one of her tirades about the dirty hippies next door.

'It's me-ee. Anyone home?'

She went through to check whether Bede was resting in the living room. Her eyes widened. One of the sofa cushions was on the floor, the other pulled aside. A pile of papers cascaded from an armchair to the floor. Two halves of a mug lay on the floor by a coffee table like a cracked egg, a stain spreading from it across the rug and trickling out onto the quarry tiles. After peering round the room, she called their names and picked her way across to the dining room where Bede's makeshift bed was. It was neatly made.

Back in the kitchen, she felt the eyes of the picture on the wall following her. Nice eyes – she'd liked Joe the couple of times she'd met him – but the sense of being watched was disconcerting. She realised it was because she hadn't seen the picture before. Hadn't their wedding photo been there? It had stuck in her mind because it was unlike any wedding photo she'd ever seen – not a suit or lacy veil in sight – but Elin had told her that was when it had been taken.

As she passed the utility room on her way out, her heart skipped a beat. His adapted wheelchair stood empty at the far end. Hadn't Elin mentioned an appointment at the hospital sometime around now? It looked like they'd simply rushed out without having time to clear up after whatever had caused the mess in the living room, or bother with the pots. Which didn't explain the flowers, but she knew Elin was stressed at the moment.

The car wasn't on the yard and she was about to leave

when she became aware of hammering from the place where they'd been working on the holiday caravan before Bede's accident.

Silvan must have spoken to them after all. Tamsin was pleased to think of him up there now, sorting it for them, and it was awesome to imagine he'd soon be living next door.

She hurried across the footbridge over the leat and made her way up the path in the direction of the sounds, pausing briefly to fuss Kip as he bustled to meet her. A metallic clacking and a curse drifted towards her. As she crested the rise in the land, Bede seemed as surprised to see her as she was him. She stopped, frowning.

'Hello, Tamsin.' He turned awkwardly on the crutches. 'Something wrong?'

'I just didn't expect... You surprised me, you know, being on your feet.'

'One of them.'

'It's an improvement. Check out your wrist! Great stuff, well done.'

'I've achieved greater things in my time.' He smiled as if to compensate. 'Actually, you've come at the right moment. This is no fun. Cop hold of that for me, will you?'

She picked up a plank, positioned it and fixed it where he instructed as he leaned on it to hold it in place. She hammered a stubborn nail at the wrong angle and it bent in two. Bede guided her patiently and she started to get the feel of it. As their work brought them close, she noticed he smelled of stale sweat, and his hair, though tied back for working, was obviously lank and unwashed. It was as out of character as the state of the house.

They worked on a couple more boards and despite the lack of conversation she began to feel the return of the camaraderie that had grown between them over the last few weeks.

'I thought Silvan was coming to help you,' she said as she picked up another board.

'Did you?'

'Didn't he have a word? You know…'

Silence.

'About helping you. With this.'

'Ah. Yes, he mentioned it.'

She waited.

'And?' Shit, he was in a mood today.

'As you can see, I'm managing.'

'So he's not, like…?'

'No. And he won't be moving in. I suppose that means you don't want to carry on. Feel free to go.'

Tamsin felt a stab of hurt on two counts – that this wasn't going to be Silvan's place and, contrarily, that Bede could think it was the only reason she was here. 'Don't talk stupid.'

He flashed her a look then shuffled back to examine what they'd done so far.

'Is Elin at the shop today?' Maybe she'd get more sense out of her when she got home.

'No.'

Tamsin suppressed a sigh. 'Where is she?'

'Did you meet Fran? Her old friend. I should say *our* friend, but I've never felt she likes me much.' Tamsin thought the name sounded familiar. 'She's gone to stay with her for a few days. Would you fetch us a cup of tea?'

Back at the house, while the kettle boiled and the tea brewed, Tamsin took the withered flowers to the compost, washed up, straightened the cushions and wiped up the spillage in the living room. She could hear her mother complaining that she never did anything like that at home without being asked, usually several times. Alderleat simply didn't look right in a mess. The fact that Elin was away seemed to explain that – he could hardly be expected to keep on top of things with his leg in plaster. Tamsin was slightly hurt that neither of them had asked her to lend a hand in Elin's absence, or at least pop round to see if he needed anything.

She poured the tea and took it out, quite proud that the mugs were still at least three-quarters full by the time she got up the path. They sat side by side on the pile of timbers to drink it.

Bede glanced down at his plastered leg, propped at an awkward angle in front of him. 'It's good to be out and about again. Good to know there's stuff I can do. Um, with your help.'

Tamsin felt a glow of satisfaction. He studied the tea in his mug, then looked up at her. 'Did we ever thank you for those skylights from your dad?'

'You should've seen Mum's face when I came home with them. I'm sure Dad only let me have them because helping you would be a way of pissing her off. Anyway, they're looking good. Glad to have helped with a bit of upcycling.'

'That's the spirit. Most of what we've done has been on a shoestring, you know, but even if I was rolling in it I wouldn't do things any differently. Saves waste.' He drained his tea, then put his mug down carefully. 'Drink up now, girl. No slacking.'

He shuffled laboriously to his feet, refusing her offer of help firmly but with a hint of gratitude. By the end of the afternoon they looked from each other to a finished wall with satisfaction.

'Nice work, thanks. Do you fancy coming back tomorrow?'

It felt like the friendliest thing he'd said to her all day. 'Sure.'

He was already on his way back to the house.

'Oh.' Back in the kitchen, he turned to look at her, eyes narrowed in reproach. 'You shouldn't have. Tidied up. I only said come and make tea.'

'What's your bloody problem today?' Tamsin finally snapped. 'I wasn't snooping around.'

'No. I never said you were. I…I'd never have sent you if I'd remembered the state the place was in, that's all.'

It seemed as close to an apology as she was likely to get. She was surprised to find she was more ready to sympathise than take offence.

'Before you go,' he said suddenly, 'could you have a quick shufty round for my glasses, please? I'm stuck without them. You know the ones. Probably in the case. Or maybe not.' He waved at the scattered papers, then began to straighten them into a pile. 'They're usually here. On the windowsill. Always here – I never lose them. It's all been weird since that bang on the head.'

She hunted around the kitchen and the living room, straightening a few more scattered objects as she went. He called to her to look upstairs, too. She hesitated; it felt uncomfortable, especially given the weirdness of his mood.

'Yes, I managed to get upstairs and sleep there last night. Progress, hey?'

Her curiosity was tinged with unease as she crossed the landing and quickly glanced around the bedroom. It was in a similar state of disarray. She picked two pillows up off the floor, edgy, half expecting to hear the clacking of his crutches behind her. The black-rimmed glasses were nowhere to be found.

By the time she came back into the kitchen he'd lined up several bottles of beer, with a glass poured and half drunk.

Sounds of him rummaging in the freezer reached her from the utility room. He called through: 'Could you feed Kip for me?'

As she set the dog's food down, she noticed the crate of empties was brimming. Bede limped through, awkwardly gripping a frost-rimed box under his arm.

'Veg stew defrosting,' he announced as he emptied it into a bowl, put it in the microwave and set the timer. Back at the kitchen table, he untied his hair and took a hearty swig from the glass. 'Sorry to send you on a wild goose chase. About the specs. Feel like I'm losing it.'

''Course you're not.' She hoped she sounded more convincing than she felt. 'Anything else I can do?'

'No, thanks.' His eyes were intense, weighing her up. 'Actually, yes. If you don't mind. Sit down.'

She drew up a chair as he leafed through the pile of papers he'd just tidied.

'Here.' He picked up an envelope – she glimpsed *Return to Sender* scrawled across it – and drew out an old eighteenth birthday card. 'I found this. In one of his books. Ex-girlfriend gave it to him; the only poetry he ever read as far as I know. I had this sudden impulse to look up a quote he liked – once I'd found my glasses, that is. This fell out.' He opened it. Holding it up at arm's length, he peered at it, narrow-eyed. 'No good. Can you read it out to me?'

She studied the blocky handwriting for a moment. *'To Niall,'* she read. 'Then the bog-standard printed birthday card stuff. *From your loving Dad* and two kisses.'

He was sitting with his face in his hands.

'What does the rest say?'

There was a note on the inside flap. *'I hope this finds you well. It's been a long time, but I remembered your 18th, at least. I know I've not kept in touch but I had my reasons. What...'*She broke off. 'It's hard to make out, sorry. Like he was upset or angry when he wrote it. *Whatever she's...told you...'* She narrowed her eyes then continued, faltering, *'Whatever she's told you I'd like to...explain for myself then it's up to you whether to forgive me. Please give me a chance. Love, Dad.* Then a note of your address and phone number.'

'Thanks,' Bede muttered. 'I couldn't make out most of it.'

'Who is it?'

He looked up. 'Could you do me one more favour?' He opened a drawer in the side of the table and from among the usual kitchen-drawer clutter took out a tattered scrap of paper, which he held out to her, glancing at the photo on the wall.

> *Bede, Elin,*
>
> *I've just popped out for a walk. Won't be gone long. Exciting times!!*
>
> *Hope things weren't too bad in the village,*
>
> *Joe x*

'This was the last thing he ever said – wrote – to us,' he said. 'So. Is it the same handwriting as the card?'

She nodded and he tucked the note away again in the back of the drawer.

'Just checking. It's obvious – I should know, shouldn't I? But...bloody glasses. Two pairs of eyes. Thanks.' He glanced at her. 'If you could have a quick scout around the yard on your way out? In case I dropped them.'

She wondered if the glasses were an excuse. If he just wanted to talk about it.

'So "Dad" is your uncle Joe? This Niall's your cousin? I didn't know—'

'Neither did I, Tamsin, neither did I.'

'How come?'

'Never told me.'

'But he was your family. I thought you were close.'

'Listen, I was fifteen when he first got in touch with me. He and my mum hadn't spoken to each other for years and he lived on his own in a flat above his hardware shop. I never thought twice about it and if I had, I'd never have asked. Shy as a sparrow I was, back then.'

'So you don't know what Joe meant about being forgiven, either?'

He gave her a withering look, which she ignored and started reading through the card again. Bede took it from her and shoved it to the bottom of the pile of papers.

'No idea. Doesn't matter.'

He picked up his beer and drained it, then reached for another bottle. Tamsin looked at the collection on the table.

'You're not going to sink all those tonight?'

'And if I do? There's whisky around somewhere, too.' He laughed mirthlessly. 'I won't embarrass you by asking you to fetch it for me. See you tomorrow. About eleven?'

'Sure.' She made one final attempt. 'Bede…?'

He was concentrating on pouring the beer into a glass. Eventually he looked up.

'Have you told Elin about this? Are you going to phone her?'

'Could do.'

'You sure you're OK?'

His smile went some way to dispersing the cloud that had settled over the room.

'Perfectly sure. Don't worry about me. Thanks, Tamsin.' The microwave pinged as though to announce her departure. 'I'll even be eating well, so you don't have to worry on that score, either.'

After closing the door, she hesitated on the threshold before walking away down the yard towards the lane. Part of her felt sorry for him; he was clearly in a bit of a state. The larger part felt relief to be away. She enjoyed his company, but even when in a better mood than this one, he was easier to deal with when Elin was around. Tamsin hoped she hadn't left because of a row.

'Hello, gorgeous.'

She jumped as she saw Silvan by the gate to the Alderleat yard.

'Hi! What are you doing here?'

'Stalking you.' He widened his eyes, grabbed her and kissed her. She relaxed into his arms, all her annoyance at his recent distance immediately melted away. 'Fancy going out tonight? We could walk along the river to Halbury. The food's great at the Queen's Arms. My treat.'

'I'd love to. Give me a moment; I'll nip and change, and think of an excuse to keep Mum happy. I've been out all afternoon without telling her.'

He brushed her cheek. 'I'll wait for as long as it takes.'

Her mother was preoccupied with paying guests and let her go with little more than a tap of her watch: half past eleven at the latest. Tamsin flung on a sundress and jacket, spent a few minutes in front of the mirror and dashed back out.

They walked arm-in-arm down the lane.

'Been out, you say?' Silvan asked. 'Anywhere exciting?'

'Helping out at Alderleat.'

'Uh-huh. How are they?'

'Elin's away. Bede was…OK. You know. Except—'

Silvan stopped and turned to her, his hands on her arms. 'He's too old for you, sweetness,' he said, eyes wide. 'Not your type. Too highly strung.'

He broke into a grin and she could feel herself blushing, even as she laughed and swiped his hands away. 'You know you're the only one for me.' Her heart flipped as he kissed her. 'So what have you been doing to piss them off? He says you're not having the caravan.'

Silvan shrugged. 'Haven't a clue. I mean, you could say it's because of them I was threatened with the sack in the first place. Northcote getting wind of the fact that I'm coming round to their point of view. Well, they can stick their stupid anti-fracking campaign from now on.'

'Don't be like that. It's not just Elin and Bede – the whole village is against it.' She frowned. 'But I'd have thought they'd have helped you out.'

'You're not the only one. I think it's come from Elin. Doesn't want me around. Listen, Tammy, can you keep a secret?'

'Cross my heart.'

'She's been coming on to me.'

'Get *off.*'

'Seriously. And when I made it clear I wasn't interested she didn't like it. So my theory is that she's blanking me, a) so he doesn't suspect anything and b) because I get the impression things aren't all sweetness and light in the Sherwell household and she's taking it out on me. People need scapegoats. And he's going along with it 'cause he doesn't want to upset her.'

Tamsin stopped. 'I don't believe it. They're not like that.'

He tugged her hand and led her over the stile, down the footpath towards the river. 'Go on then, you're their best mate. What do you think?'

'I think they just want it as a holiday cottage. They need the money. He told me.'

'Those two do *not* need money. Have you seen all they've got there?'

She felt inexplicably defensive. 'They've put a lot of work into it. On a shoestring.'

He laughed. 'Bollocks. It's all inherited; didn't you know?'

'From Bede's uncle? That's only part of it. They're still, like, paying it off. I've heard them talking about it.'

'Really? What have they told you? I heard that uncle – Joe, wasn't it? – drowned in the flood a couple of years back. Maybe they're hiding something.' He pulled a theatrical face. 'Died in mysterious circumstances.'

'You're not suggesting they did away with him for his house and money!'

He raised his eyebrows.

'You. Are. Joking. No, it's not even funny.'

She quickened her pace and walked ahead.

'You've got to admit, Tammy, they're driven. Him in particular. Fucking obsessed. Maybe Joe wanted to call time on all that eco stuff. Imagine the lengths a man on a mission would go to. You've said yourself Bede's unpredictable. And what about her? Do you think she *liked* sharing a home with her husband's uncle?'

They were at the river's edge. She stopped and gazed into the fast-flowing water. Silvan stood beside her and put his arm round her.

'I'm not having it,' she said. 'I dunno how you can even think it. Only this afternoon he was getting all emotional about Joe. Weirded me out a bit to be honest.'

'Yeah? What was that about?'

Tamsin pictured Bede's haunted eyes and felt slightly guilty about betraying him as she said, 'He found this birthday card. Seems Joe had a son Bede didn't know about Can you believe it?'

Silvan laughed dismissively. 'What's to believe? Sons send dads birthday cards all the time.'

'No, this was *from* Joe. Returned unopened. Sad, isn't it?'

'S'pose. None of our business. What do I care?'

'Oh, you've got no heart.' She nudged him playfully, relieved he wasn't going to push her to say more, and changed the subject. 'Anyway, hope you don't mind, but I said I'd go back and help again tomorrow. It doesn't bother you, does it?'

He took her hand, drew her to him and kissed her lightly.

'Why would it? Just watch him, Tammy. There's something about that man I don't trust.' He began walking. 'Let's get a move on. I'm starving. And we're celebrating.' He grinned at her. 'I've been saving the good news. You can do what you like at Alder-bloody-leat and I won't give a toss. You know I said they could stuff their campaign? I've sweet-talked Northcote into keeping me on while he's got bigger things on his mind. You can go off and enjoy your family holiday safe in the knowledge I'll be here waiting for you when you get home.'

10th December, 2001

So I guess I'm not going back. Don't know which makes me sadder, losing Sophie or leaving the community, the family I thought I was becoming part of. Suppose that'll break up any day now, though. The road scheme's going to win, they always do.

'Joseph,' she says. She has this thing about always calling people by their full names. Graham, Francine, Stephen. (I'll never forget when Bede apologised, first weekend he was there, for only having one syllable. Didn't get them off to a good start.) 'I was picking your jacket up off the floor.'

She gives me this look. It wasn't the usual stuff about me being a bit tidier. No, she was holding up my wallet that had slipped out of the pocket, waving my photo of Suzie and the kids in my face. Taken a few weeks before I left, it was; our Emma's 8 and Niall only 5. My heart sank.

'So?' she says. 'Who are they?'

I'm staring at her, mind blank. Can't think of a convincing story, but don't want to lie. I mumbled something about my ex-wife and kids.

'Ex?' she says. 'So why are you carrying it around?'

I found it the other day when I was packing up to move to Alderleat, just put it in my wallet without thinking. Don't know why, it only breaks my heart. I told Sophie we'd been apart for three years – three years already! Hard to believe – and there was no way I'd have some sordid affair behind her or Suzie's back.

This hard look comes into her eyes. 'Why didn't you tell me? Why did you split up?'

'It never came up so I didn't see no reason to tell you. Why we split? We argued.'

'What about?'

'Stuff.' My mind racing. She's suddenly on at me, insisting she wants to know. I just kept saying it was over and showed her my empty ring finger. You can probably just still see the trace if you know you're looking – old and faded enough to be in the past not just removed for the weekend.

'So if it's over what's the harm in telling me?'

Jesus, there are times I wonder why I didn't chuck her out the car when she was giving it out about my bacon sarnie.

'If it's over why do you need to know?'

She reminded me about Kelly. The woman's neurotic, but even so, she didn't deserve that. She turned up a couple of weeks ago in floods of tears. Her boyfriend of several years started behaving weirdly then just upped and disappeared without trace. They suspect he was some kind of infiltrator, a government spy, can you believe? As if anyone would want to spy on a group of environment protesters. But Grey and people he knows seem to think it's for real.

'So come on, Joseph,' Sophie says. 'Out with it. Tell me why you left your wife. Otherwise how do I know you did? That you're not one of them?'

I couldn't believe what I was hearing. I've done my bloody best to make up for what happened back then, to be a decent fella, and whatever I do people still think the worst of me. Not just people. Sophie, who's supposed to love me. I could feel the rage bubbling under.

'Say that again.'

And she stares me out, tears in her eyes, and asks me

again. Tell me why. I'm not proud of myself and God help me if anyone reads this. I lost it with her. Totally lost it. Grabbed her and shook her and yelled how can you think that of me you heartless bitch, doesn't what we had mean anything? It's in the fucking past, just leave it, what the hell does it matter?! She opened her mouth to argue and I slapped her. Then I froze. Felt sick.

She looks at me and says, well I got my answer, didn't I?

Turns away.

That's it. The photo's gone, burned, ashes trampled into the ground, same as this page probably will be once I've got it out my system.

There's no way I'm telling our Bede. I'd been wondering whether he ought to know about Suzie and the kids, but this settles it. I'm sorry but I just couldn't stand to risk losing someone else. I feel bad about keeping stuff from him, but he should be glad he's come to mean that much to me.

Something unforgivable

Bede woke with a sense of purpose. A headache nagged in the background, though it was no worse than usual and probably not as bad as he deserved. As he slugged down the painkillers, the thought of the beer bottles and unwashed plate downstairs filled him with momentary shame. Tough; it could wait. He caught sight of himself in the mirror and disgusted himself even more. That, he should do something about. The ungainly hassle of trying to keep the cast dry and the extra time it took were frustrating, but he felt better after a shower. A quick coffee and bowl of muesli brought him almost back to humanity, while adding to the kitchen chaos. Before deliberately turning his back on it, he checked the house phone and his mobile. No message from Elin. It made him feel slightly better about not calling her.

Outside, he paused to cut some flowers. The small bouquet looked a bit ragged, nothing like the one Elin would have conjured up, but he was satisfied. He stowed the flowers, with the crutches, behind the seat of the tractor. The fresh air cleared away the final cobwebs as he set off. He hadn't been sure if he'd be able to drive, but he found it surprisingly easy – clambering in had been the hardest part. It may have been medically and legally forbidden, but he wasn't going far so what the heck. He wouldn't be a danger to anyone. As he turned out onto the road, he braced himself for the fears to return. It felt fine. It might be different when he encountered another vehicle, but this had to be done.

He became aware of a presence behind him and realised Kip had jumped in. Damn; he'd meant to leave him at home. He tried to remember whether he'd fed him that morning. Had he really become so self-absorbed that he'd neglect his dog? It was too late to turn back now; Marjorie liked to see Kip in any case.

A light rain spotted the windscreen of the cab with increasing intensity, blowing in the open side. He turned the wipers on, wondering whether Tamsin would turn up in this weather, and whether in fact he wanted her to. Eleven, they'd agreed. He might be late back, and she was unlikely to wait long. Feeling detached, he weighed up the advantages of solitude compared with companionship and help. Let her stay or go; he had no intention of cutting this visit short.

On the straight between Holtwood and the bridge, he glanced dispassionately at the roadside where they said they'd found him. Grass verge and hedge; it meant nothing. He held back at the bridge to let a car cross. Safe in the cab of the tractor, it was easy to deflect the sensation of the car veering towards him.

As he crossed the humped back of the bridge, he glanced down, aware of the energy of the river sliding beneath. His breath caught momentarily. Glad to find he was still capable of feeling after all, he indicated at the track to Bridge Farm.

Partway down, he met Northcote's Bentley coming the other way. He swore, stopped and waited for him to reverse; they were about three-quarters of the way to the house, and there was nowhere for Bede to pull in and let him pass. Philip flashed and blared the horn, gesticulating impatiently. Though he knew he was never going to win, Bede allowed the stand-off to continue for a few moments. As Philip opened the door, he threw the tractor in reverse and turned awkwardly in his seat, trying not to smile to himself as he rolled back towards the lane entrance, then pulled over. Philip drew level, blocking his way, and swished the window down.

'What are you doing here?'

'Morning, Philip. I'm paying a visit to my friend.'

'My mother's unwell. Certainly not in a position to receive visitors. I'm coming back this afternoon; I'll pass on your regards, shall I?'

'She doesn't have to go to any trouble to "receive" me. I'm sure she'd appreciate a visit.'

'For goodness' sake, Sherwell, can't you leave her alone?'

'It's Marjorie I want to see, not you. If you could just let me past.'

More impatient than Bede, Kip jumped down from the cab and started nosing around the top of the lane.

'Keep your bloody dog under control!'

Bede called, annoyed that he had to snap his order out twice before Kip obeyed and jumped back onto the tractor.

'And I suggest you keep your wife under control as well.'

If he'd dragged him from the tractor and punched him it couldn't have winded him more effectively.

'What...what the hell is that supposed to mean?'

'You know perfectly well. But more importantly, I hear you're still slandering me. Still insinuating I had something to do with your unfortunate accident. It doesn't say much for your case that you need to stoop to such allegations. But feelings are running high and people might even believe you. So I've told your wife and I'm telling you – if the pair of you don't put a stop to your evil accusations, I'll have to do something serious about it.'

Without a further word, Philip revved and sped off, pulling out dangerously fast onto the road. Bede made his way down to the farmhouse, replaying the conversation, trying to decipher whether Philip's comment about his wife referred to anything other than the 'insinuations'. And what about those? He didn't recall saying anything recently; maybe he should have a word with Elin. In good time; he had other things on his mind right now.

He knocked, paused then let himself in. Marjorie was pottering with her plants in the conservatory. She waved away his concerns about the chest infection she seemed unable to shake off. 'He shouldn't have said anything. I have my bad days and this isn't one of them.'

So much for not being well enough to see him.

'On the other hand, I'm glad to see *you* out and about,' she said. 'Don't worry about Kip. Bring him through.'

Indicating a chair, she helped with the crutches, fetched him a footstool despite his protests and made a fuss of the flowers that had got slightly crushed when he'd wedged them under his arm. He thanked her in turn for the get-well card and the bottle of single malt that he felt guilty about goading Tamsin with last night.

Marjorie disappeared to the kitchen to make tea, leaving Bede wondering how well she actually was and should he really bother her with the conversation he intended to have. When she returned with a tray of tea things, the flowers looking a little more respectable in a vase, her sprightliness dispelled his doubts.

'Elin sends her love.' A harmless white lie – she would have if she'd known he was coming. They reminisced for a few moments about the time when Marjorie had met Fran, neither of them mentioning the recent planning decision. Bede suspected Marjorie would be on their side if asked, but understood if she wanted to remain neutral. She poured the tea and sat in her usual chair. He praised the plants in the conservatory, reluctant to appear too hasty or self-centred.

'Just look at the gorgeous orange tree Joe bought me,' she said. 'The birthday before he died, remember? It's doing so well. I think of him whenever it flowers; that wonderful scent.'

He forced a smile. Thanking her silently for the opening, he steeled himself to speak.

'Marjorie...I've just found out... Did you know Joe had a son?'

She regarded him steadily and put her teacup down. 'So he didn't tell you.'

'No.' Bede felt hollow. She knew. He stared unfocused out to the garden, trying to suppress his anger and feeling of betrayal. Hadn't he wanted answers? Not with this horrid sense of backs turned, whispering, exclusion. But what had he been expecting – that he and Marjorie would join forces to unravel some great mystery together? 'No, he didn't.'

'I'm sorry, Bede. I suppose that means you didn't know about Suzanne, either?'

He shook his head wordlessly.

'His wife.'

Should have thought of that one. 'What the hell's going on?'

She regarded him with the stern expression that always brought him back down to earth. 'Nothing's "going on". He swore me to secrecy, and I didn't want to betray him, though I tried to persuade him to tell you about his family. But it doesn't make much difference now, does it?'

'You tell me.' Bede tried to steady his voice. 'So what's the story?'

She studied him before speaking. 'Joe was estranged from her by the time I met him. Back in the late 90s, that was –

about the time your mother died and he got in touch with you. They had two children. Something awful had happened and Suzanne threw him out. She wouldn't let him have anything to do with the children, which upset him horribly. He bought them cards and presents for birthdays and Christmas. They moved house, but he tracked down the address. He gave up sending them after a couple of years, though. Suzanne always returned them unopened. I suggested he gave the presents to a charity shop.'

She picked up her teacup. Bede's mouth felt dry, but he couldn't bring himself to drink.

'I kept suggesting he should tell you. Once the three of you were settled at Alderleat, I knew it would be a shock to you if his children got in touch. Better to talk to you first. He obviously didn't. How did you find out?'

Bede reached into his jacket pocket and took out the birthday card. 'I was looking for something the other day. Came across this.'

She took it from him, picked up her glasses from a side table and read it. 'I'm sorry you had to find out that way,' she said as she lowered it.

His resentment flared up again. '*You* didn't bloody well tell me either.'

She drew herself up; she could still look formidable despite her age. 'I hardly think it was my business to.' Her expression softened. 'They meant nothing to you and practically, Alderleat was as much yours and Elin's as Joe's. I witnessed his will, so I knew he didn't mention them in it – part of me wasn't surprised, the way she cut him off, but I tried to suggest he should see his children right. He was having none of it – he assumed she'd have poisoned them against him. Anyway, you had nothing to lose, and nothing to gain by knowing.'

'What was he supposed to have done that was so awful, for God's sake?'

Marjorie shook her head. 'I've got no idea. He was always a good enough man in my experience. I've sometimes wondered if you might be able to shed some light on that, at least. When he told me about making his peace with your mother before she died, he mentioned "something unforgivable" that had come between them, but he never said what it was.'

Bede thought back. During one visit to his mum's hospice bedside, as he braved the veneer of cheer and kindness thinly cloaking the inevitability of death, she'd asked him to pass her handbag from the bedside cabinet.

'I suppose we ought to tell that renegade brother of mine that I'm at death's door. I know things haven't always been easy for you.' She waved a hand towards the corridor his stepfather had just left down. 'Though God knows I tried. I'm not making any promises, but Joe might be a friend to you. He should, if he's got any sense of right and wrong.' She'd produced a notebook and showed him a phone number to copy down. 'It's a bit late now to forgive and forget, but tell him I'd like to see him.'

'Forgive and forget what?'

Since she'd been ill she often lost her train of thought and fell silent, but Bede suspected this time it was deliberate.

He stared now at the tiles of the conservatory floor. *Forgive and forget what?* Marjorie waited. 'She never told me anything,' he said eventually. 'So, first he was spurned by Mum, then this family of his.' He glared at Marjorie as if she too had rejected Joe. 'What the fuck did he do to deserve it?'

'Watch your language, young man.'

The absurdity of the comment made him snort with laughter. He caught the gleam in her eye and realised she'd done it on purpose.

'That's better, get it out of your system.' She pressed a cup into his hands. He tried to sip his tea but felt choked by a lump in his throat. He spluttered ungraciously and put it down.

'Maybe you should try and find her. His ex-wife. Ask her. It might not be as bad as you think.'

'Do I want to know?'

'I can't tell you. Think about it. Leave it a while, calm down.' She squeezed his hand, which he realised she'd grasped. 'Talk to Elin about it.'

Despite her encouraging words and comforting, grandmotherly hug as he left, Bede felt unclean as he drove away. Nothing had actually happened, yet he was a completely different person. *Something unforgivable.* As he turned out onto the road to head for home, he realised he was hunched in the tractor cab as if making himself smaller, less noticeable, as his mum had told him off for doing in his lanky teenager days.

Back at Alderleat, Kip jumped out of the cab before he'd finished parking up, and ran towards the road. Bede called, but the wind-borne scent was stronger than obedience. The dog paused, looked back at him and continued. The second time he'd ignored him this morning. As he grappled with the crutches in the rain, frustration grew and he yelled the dog's name in a torrent of swearing. By the time he was steadied, Kip cowering at his feet as he shook his collar like a madman, Bede felt ashamed. He tried to justify himself by calling to mind the dangers of speeding cars on the lane, exacerbated by puddled rain on the asphalt, but he wasn't fooling himself. He'd simply lost it.

Tamsin emerged from the greenhouse. Mercifully, she

hadn't witnessed his outburst or, more likely, was making a good job of smiling pretence. He limped over, wondering how he could tactfully ask her to leave.

She tapped her watch. 'Time do you call this?'

He looked at his own.

'Twenty to twelve.'

'Not funny. Shit, Bede, you look worse than yesterday. If you would insist on drinking all that beer and whisky. Dickhead. I told you—'

'Less of the lip.' He gazed at the ground, then waved toward the greenhouse. 'Thanks for doing that. Elin'd be grateful. And if you must know I'm not in the least bit hungover. Didn't touch the whisky. Bit of a headache but that's a fact of life these days.'

'So what's wrong?'

By the look on her face, he'd have his work cut out to fob her off. No way was he ready to talk to anyone about his conversation with Marjorie, so he gave her a blow-by-blow account of his run-in with Philip Northcote, knowing she'd sympathise.

'Anyway, I'm sorry, I've got stuff I need to do. Won't be ready to go up to the caravan till this afternoon. I'll manage. Sorry for messing up the arrangements. Come in, I'll pay you for what you've done.'

'I don't mind carrying on with the plants while I wait,' she said as they went into the house. 'I could throw us a salad together for lunch if you like. There's stuff growing in the greenhouse that's getting past its best.'

He shrugged. 'How could I refuse? But you do know we can only afford—'

'It's not all about the money. We're off tomorrow for a week's holiday. Might as well give you a bit more help before we go. My choice.'

'Thanks. I appreciate it.' Leaving her to it, he went through to the living room and switched on the laptop. As it booted up, he picked up his glasses and put them on.

He stared at the case in his hand.

'Tamsin, you there?'

She appeared in the doorway. 'You found them! Great stuff. Where were they?'

'I was going to ask you. Just here. On the desk. One of the first places I looked.'

'Me too. Deffo weren't there yesterday; I searched all over it, even opened the drawers. Felt guilty about intruding, you know?'

He glared at the desk as if it had come alive and started swallowing objects, then grown a mouth and begun laughing at him.

'You must have found them and put them there when you were half asleep or pissed or whatever.'

'I didn't get that bloody pissed!'

He slammed the glasses case down on the desk. Everything – every little thing – felt out of control. Crazy, mad, losing it – this must be what it felt like. He reached for the phone and dialled Elin's number. Unsurprised when it went straight to voicemail, he couldn't bring himself to leave a message.

Sounds of doing indicated that Tamsin had retreated to the kitchen. Bede smiled grimly. Poor girl was probably terrified. Well, he wasn't asking her to stay; she was free to leave any time she liked.

He googled Suzanne Sherwell; found very little except a Facebook page. He hardly thought a friend request was appropriate, so all he saw was a profile picture and that she lived in Leeds. The same neck of the woods that both he and Joe had come from. He studied the photo; tried to memorise the features. Emma Sherwell was a designer of some kind in London. As far as he could tell from the photos on her website, she looked like her mother. He thought he could see Joe in her, too, but Elin was better at seeing resemblances than he was.

There was a family photo – mother, sister and cheeky blond little brother – on one of Emma's blog posts about a couple of childhood holidays that had influenced her work. The picture was too small to tell him much about the Niall in the birthday card, but as he read the text, Bede found that the failure to mention a father stung him more than it should have.

'Ready when you are.'

Tamsin's footsteps approached and the Alderleat watermill filled the screen as he hastily switched to the desktop.

'I wasn't going to look.' Was he that transparent? 'It's salad so it can wait. I'll be in the greenhouse; just say the word.'

'No, no. I'm done here.'

A snap decision: these people meant nothing to him. He'd seen enough. He closed down the computer and tried to shut off his thoughts as conclusively.

It was going well despite the rain that had been falling steadily all afternoon. At least that proved the roof was sound. Bede was checking through the stack of timbers to choose the tongue-and-groove boards for the next section while Tamsin went to fetch a drink.

'Is Kip with you?' he asked her when she returned.

'Haven't seen him since we came out here.' She handed him his tea.

He looked around and called. 'That dog's got more bloody disobedient since I've been laid up. Taking advantage of the state I'm in to behave like a naughty kid. We need some serious training sessions.' He put his mug down. ''Scuse me a minute.'

He limped up the path a little, anger cranking up his voice as he yelled the dog's name. The wind in the trees and rain pattering on his hood were the only response. He was beginning to despair when he saw Kip come running. Suppressed relief made his reprimand all the harsher.

'Biggest incentive I've had so far to get my act together, isn't it?' he said when he returned. 'Don't want to think I'm traumatising my dog on top of everything else. Come on, back to work.'

'You haven't drunk your tea yet. It'll be cold.'

He picked up his mug and drained it. It was cold. 'See what I mean about getting my act together?'

They settled into the rhythm they'd established of choose, position, brace, nail, accompanied by music from the battery-powered docking station she'd brought. It was going well; he even allowed himself to think they might have all the walls lined by the end of the afternoon. Tamsin timed the hammering to the music and was singing along. He was almost tempted to join in.

'Bede?'

Something was askew. He found he was sitting against the wall, looking up at the girl's worried face. The grey sky glared through the skylight above her and a now-familiar pain stabbed from the back of his head to his eyes. He closed them.

'You all right?'

He nodded.

'You had me worried there. You just froze, like there was

nobody home, then you were like, "When's Elin coming with those papers?"'

'Shit. Thought I'd managed to put all that blackout crap behind me.'

She tried to look reassuring. 'It was only a few seconds. I suggested you sat down for a bit and here you are.'

'Thanks. I'm fine now.' He forced a smile and she helped him to his feet, handed him the crutches. 'That's it for today, I'm afraid. This headache's going to get worse. Need to go in and lie down.'

Tamsin offered to stay behind and clear up. He could feel her watching him as he made his way to the house, despite his protestations that he was perfectly capable. Once safely across the bridge over the leat, he turned to stare into the rushing water. Felt nothing. He reminded himself he didn't believe in ghosts, spirits, apparitions. It didn't stop him yelling 'I wouldn't believe a word you told me anyway!' into the fine, rain-mingled spray. The stream rushed by and the spray hung on the air unchanged.

He was at the door of the house when he heard tyres on the yard. For once he hoped he really was hallucinating. If he slipped inside without looking round, maybe whoever it was would leave him alone. He heard Silvan call his name. Hunched his shoulders. The jeep door slammed, triggering a pounding crack in his brain.

'Everything OK, mate?'

'Mm hm.' Without turning his head, he waved a crutch towards the caravan. 'Tamsin's over there.'

'I'll go see her soon. But you look—'

'Blackout just now.' He kept his back resolutely turned. 'I'm fine. Go.'

'You sound shaky. You need to sit down.'

'Where do you think I'm going?' He opened the door.

Silvan was straight in behind him. Drained of the energy to object, Bede went over to the kitchen counter, fumbled for a couple of painkillers and poured himself a glass of water. 'Close the door on your way out.'

'I can understand you're not thrilled to see me. But that's why I wanted a word. Like, apologise if I came on a bit strong the other day. I said some things I probably shouldn't have.'

'Yes. You did.' He closed his eyes against the glare from the window.

'I'm sorry, mate. Seriously. Can we shake on it?'

Bede kept his hands gripped tightly around the crutches. 'I'm not in the mood for this. Need to lie down.'

He shuffled past Silvan into the living room and sank onto the sofa. Sleep was beginning to take him over when he heard Tamsin's voice and the welcome patter of claws on the kitchen floor.

'Sorry to disturb you. I've brought Kip home.'

Damn. He'd forgotten about the dog. He was unsure whether he was more grateful to Tamsin for delivering him safely back or for being there to take Silvan away. He reached out a hand to touch the reality of his dog's coat; the warm presence was comforting but he wished Elin was there, that things could be back to the way they had been. He drifted to sleep on a wave of love that wounded like a knife, forming vague intentions of talking to her, making it right.

Not what matters

It had been a dispiriting day. Soaked by relentless rain, they'd been splashed with mud, insulted, ignored, threatened. And achieved nothing. A new court injunction kept them at a distance from the site entrance, and the test drilling would be going ahead.

'You lot have just been on telly again,' Jeff announced as they walked in. 'Don't worry, I recorded it.'

'I hope we looked more glam than we feel,' Fran said as she took off her coat and shoes.

'Came across quite well,' he said. 'That reporter woman seems to be on your side.'

'Don't get excited,' Elin said. 'I stayed well away this time.'

'Don't go all coy. You were amazing the way you stood up to your friend Northcote the other day,' Fran said, waving to Jeff to pour Elin a glass of wine.

'It was hardly the most eloquent debate I've ever had.' Elin took the wine gratefully.

'Sounded effective enough to me.' Fran smiled, eyeing Elin's wine glass ruefully. 'You don't know how much I crave one of those.'

'Abstinence must be hard at a time like this,' Jeff said, 'but it's all in a good cause.' He gave Elin a worried look. She wished he'd realise that she wasn't about to dissolve in a heap every time they referred to Fran's pregnancy.

They went through to the living room and Fran threw herself onto the sofa, playing the decadent princess as Jeff supplied her with cushions and one of his magic fruit juice concoctions. Elin flopped into an armchair and put her feet up.

'Talking of good causes,' he said, 'Bede phoned, about half an hour ago, just as I got in from work.'

After a spell of ignoring his missed calls, Elin's hurt and self-righteous anger were beginning to turn to guilt as she wondered whether something had happened. But she'd sent him a message saying she'd be back the next day; he could wait. Let him stew. 'What did he want?'

'I'm not sure, really, apart from checking you were going home tomorrow. I tried to get him talking. You know what he's like. He more or less ignored me; asked if you could call him back.'

'He knows I'll be there tomorrow,' she said. 'It won't be anything I want to discuss on the phone.'

'Elin…' Fran looked concerned. 'He rang our landline. He never does that. Don't you think you should see what it's about?'

'Yeah, he sounded a bit weird,' Jeff put in. 'Weirder than usual.'

Fran batted him with a cushion. 'Not nice.'

'Dinner's ready as soon as you've rung,' he offered by way of apology.

'It smells delicious,' Elin said. 'I'm going to enjoy my final meal with you two in peace. He can wait. Talk about attention seeking.'

Fran was holding the phone out to her. 'You don't have to be on for long. You'll only worry all evening if you don't speak to him.'

'Will I?'

The regular headlights of oncoming cars dazzled her with monotonous regularity. Elin hated motorways and the driving rain was elevating it to headache level. Every time she passed a lorry the blinding spray made her feel as though she were plunging into the unknown for the seconds it took until the wipers swooped in to rescue her.

With a stretch of clear road ahead, she fumbled and shoved a CD into the slot. The bloody No Surrender demo. It didn't matter; she just needed to drive out the refrain in her head: 'Kip's dead.'

The news had floored her; she knew how Bede would be feeling. The road became even more blurred as tears compounded the effect of rain on the windscreen. She imagined their beloved dog's body – limp? stiff? – silky fur soaked with blood and slime. Bede hadn't gone into details. She didn't have to see. He'd already buried him behind the mill.

He'd said there was something else but he wanted to wait until they were together. She deliberately untensed her shoulders. That voice: if he intended to talk about reconciliation, he sounded bleak about it. She pulled out to overtake a bunch of slow-moving trucks. A pair of bright lights appeared behind her with a flash of aggression. She gripped the steering wheel to prevent herself from swerving. A cold fear took hold of her. Normally she'd have given them the finger and maintained her speed, or even slowed, but tonight she put on a spurt and swerved in as soon as she could to let the idiot past.

The house was in darkness. Elin parked next to the side door into the kitchen, drew her coat around her and raised her hood. The door was locked. She dived back into the car and found her keys. It was bolted. She knocked, called Bede's name, knocked again, then went round to the front door. That, too, was barred like a fortress. She couldn't recall them ever using the bolts.

The steady roar of the leat merged with the pattering of rain on her hood as she went to the living-room window. The curtains were drawn but there was a faint crack down one side. She peered in. A flickering glow infused the room from the fireplace, out of sight. As her eyes got used to the darkness, she saw Bede sitting on the sofa, bent forward, head in hands. She tapped on the window and he looked up. He lowered his head again. She knocked more forcefully, and called. He reached for the crutches, stood, and moved out of her line of sight. The fireglow swelled momentarily then was dimmed by the halting shadow of him crossing the room to the window. He tugged at the curtain to cover the crack. Soaking by now, she hammered on the window and yelled his name. He yanked the curtain back, eyes wide.

'Elin!'

He motioned towards the door and she waited there, the din of water coming at her from all angles, as she listened to him rattling the bolts aside. It took a while; they were stiff with disuse. She was surprised they were still aligned. He opened the door.

'Quick!'

She had hardly stepped in when he shut the door behind her and turned the key.

'Take your wet things off. Fire's lit.'

He turned back to the door, slid one bolt across and rattled the door in its frame as he tried to shove the other into its slot. He gave up and turned. He looked haggard, worse than she'd feared. She moved to hug him, all resentment gone, but he stepped back.

'What's going on, Bede? Why did you lock me out?'

'It wasn't you. I had to lock it. I'm not safe. We're not safe.'

'What on earth…?'

'He didn't get me, but he got my dog. He won't be satisfied till we've gone…one way or another. I can't tell you how relieved I am that you're here, safe.'

'So you bolted the door on me. I said I was coming straight back.'

'Not till late. You must've driven like a maniac.'

'I said over three hours ago, after…after you told me about Kip, that I was setting off straight away.' She turned back towards the door. 'I need—'

'No.' His hand shot out and grabbed her arm. 'Don't go.'

'I've no intention of going.'

'You should get your wet things off.'

She drew her arm from his grasp, frowning at him. 'I need to get my bag from the car.'

'Can't it wait?'

'I think I left the car door open.' She gave him an accusing look. 'I was distracted by trying all the doors and windows.'

'For fuck's sake. Hurry up, then. And lock up when you get back.'

She reached for the outside light switch.

'Don't.'

She switched it on in defiance; by the time she'd unbolted and opened the door he'd turned it off again. There was no point in a pantomime routine; she grabbed the torch they kept on a shelf by the door and went to fetch her bag. When she returned, half expecting to find the door locked against her, she secured it, took her bag to the bottom of the stairs and removed her sodden coat.

'I've put the kettle on for you,' he called. 'You'll need a hot drink to warm you up.'

His voice, and the thought, sounded reassuringly his own.

'Thanks.'

She went through to the kitchen and hung her coat on the back of a chair to dry. Apart from her own wet footprints, the room was spotlessly clean. It seemed strangely silent. After a few moments she realised why: the hum of the boiler from the utility room was absent, and the kettle was dry and cold. She took it to the sink to fill it up. As she turned the tap on, she heard him call.

'In here. Turn everything off and come through.'

Bewildered, she did as he said. The living room was lit only by the fire burning brightly in the woodburner. In the semi-darkness the room looked as neat as the kitchen, apart from a pile of books, papers and old clothes by the fire. She moved to switch a lamp on.

'Leave it. Come and sit down, for goodness' sake.'

She stayed standing in the doorway.

'What's going on, Bede?'

'It's all in here.' He waved at the fireplace, where wisps of steam were beginning to escape from the stove-top kettle. 'We've used far too much recently. It's high time to put things right.'

'What are you talking about?'

'All the extra light and heat I've wasted being ill, all the car journeys back and forth, everything. There's a balance needs setting right.'

'But it's all ours, produced sustainably.'

'Over-use, Elin. Things. Things that wear out, things

that need replacing. However we might like to pretend with "clean" alternatives, we're still surrounded by excess consumption. I've been as guilty as anyone and I need to change.' He waved a hand in frustration. 'I'll explain more when I've got my head straight. For now, can't you just accept how I feel without making me justify myself?'

She was finding it harder by the minute. 'But what's that heap?'

He followed her gaze towards the fireplace. 'Stuff that needs getting rid of. Thought I might as well use it for fuel. Kill two birds with one stone.'

'Thought you were against killing birds,' she muttered.

He looked at her, stung. 'I don't know how you can joke at a time like this.'

'Sorry. Release of nervous tension.'

'What do you mean, nervous?' He leaned forward, agitated. 'What do you think I'm going to *do*?'

'Not you. Everything. All this.'

She wondered whether to join him on the sofa or sit down in the armchair across the room. The kettle emitted a faint whistle and she poured water on the tea bags in two mugs.

'It's not nice, is it? Not understanding, not knowing.' He laughed harshly. 'Steve didn't get anywhere either, you know. Can't either of you say what you mean? Tried to make out he was just here because of the job. I told him I knew, but it was obvious you'd got there first.'

'It was only natural that I'd have spoken to him.'

'Of course. Which is why it was so pathetic that he was rambling on as if nothing had happened. Like you are now.' He shook his head. 'Then I've got Northcote telling me to keep my wife under control. What's that about?'

'If you weren't so stubborn about not having a TV in the

house, you might have seen the news.' She began to tell him about the protest and Philip's involvement. His indifference stung. It may only have been on the local news, but he could have followed their actions online, at least. 'I could tell you more, but you don't look remotely interested.'

'What do you expect?'

'I'd hoped we could talk.'

His expression was unreadable. 'I wanted to make sure you're safe. I imagine we're both upset about Kip. But as for the rest…' He shifted his position. 'Sit down, El.'

She finished making the tea, handed him a mug, then sat in the armchair across from him. The quiet crackling of the fire filled the silence. A third warm presence, who might have helped bridge the gap, was missing and everything else suddenly seemed petty.

'I still can't believe Kip isn't here,' she said quietly. 'Tell me what happened.'

The firelight flickered shadows across his features. His hand fretted restlessly at the arm of the sofa.

'Poor lad,' he said. 'I loved him, right to the end. None of it affected the way I felt.'

She felt lost again. 'None of what?'

'He was Joe's dog, wasn't he?' He waved in dismissal. 'All in good time. You asked what happened. He was missing for a while yesterday afternoon. After I found out…' Bede studied his hand. 'And again this morning. It felt like an omen. Not that I believe in them. But it did. I had this mad idea that as soon as I accepted everything, he'd be back. Maybe I just realised too late.'

'Realised what?'

'I had a blackout, yesterday. When I thought they were all over. Slept for hours. When I woke up, he'd disappeared again. Must've let him out during the night when I was half-asleep. Except I don't sleepwalk, do I? As well as vanishing, he'd been generally playing up, you know? Like I'm acting all weird with all this shit, so he's acting up too. When I got up to find him gone I didn't think twice, just assumed he'd be back when he'd had enough pissing me off.' He buried his face in his hands. 'Can't believe I…'

Rain rattled against the window pane as she wondered how to respond. He lowered his hands, eyes fixed on the ground.

'So I didn't go out to look straight away. I spent the morning cleaning, as if that'd make it right. I'd let things go. Let myself go. I don't believe in omens but… If something comes from inside yourself, that's just as real, isn't it? I made the place spotless – for you, too. Didn't want you to come back to… I kept thinking as soon as I'd finished, he'd be back. That's what an omen is, something that makes you think and take notice.'

His hand was sweeping the arm of the sofa in a constant motion of brushing away imaginary dirt.

'About lunch time, there's a knock on the door. Silvan and Tamsin. Bloody panic-stricken. They'd been on their way up to the caravan, to surprise me by doing some work there. And there…in the leat…caught up on the water wheel… He was already dead; God knows how long he'd been there. Well, since last night. This morning? Must've let him out some time. Maybe I even drove him away. Can't remember a fucking thing. Oh, Elin, how long is this going to go on for? So many gaps…scraps of memory, chunks of my life…gone.'

He looked at his hand, still now, on the arm of the sofa.

'They were great, both of them. Helped me get him out. Well, got him out for me.' He waved a disparaging hand at his plastered leg. 'Not much use, was I? He'd been round yesterday, Silvan had, apologising for the way he'd been, and

I didn't want to know, but I was grateful they were both here this morning.'

He looked up, and at last met her eye.

'I'm sorry I wasn't,' she said.

'I'm glad you didn't see it. The way I was with that poor bloody dog when I got home yesterday lunch time. Everything was getting to me and I lost it. I'm sure Tamsin saw. And…and as we sat there round the kitchen table over mugs of tea, I could see her remembering it. Wondering… And I wondered…'

'Bede, don't.' Shocked, she wanted to move over and sit by him. A slight shake of his head kept her where she was. 'I know you'd never harm that dog.'

'I don't know anything any more. But there's one thing I do bloody remember. I met fucking Northcote on Marjorie's track yesterday and he made some remark about keeping my dog under control then told me to watch it. What kind of cold-blooded sicko would use a dog like that? So I just don't feel safe. Sorry for locking you out.'

She wished she knew of a way to close the distance between them, and where to begin with all the questions his rambling account made her want to ask.

'Put some more stuff on the fire,' he said.

She opened the stove door. The smell was acrid. 'What have you got on here?'

He gave a harsh laugh. 'Shoes burn well, but they stink a bit.'

'And cause a fair amount of pollution.'

'I'm not in the mood, Elin.'

Shaking her head, she picked up a boot, the companion of which was presumably producing the smell. She frowned. 'All this is Joe's. These books, these photos. You're not burning them?'

'Got to go.'

'We sorted through everything. We only kept things we could use or stuff with sentimental value.'

'That was when I thought it mattered.'

Elin reluctantly put the second boot on the fire, watching the flames take hold. She could see the charred remains of photos among the ashes that had drifted out to the hearth. Refusing to add to them, she ignored Bede's protests and reached instead for a log from the basket. The photo on top of the pile tugged at her heart: Bede, around sixteen, with a fishing rod and his first trout, pride lighting up his face. Imagining Joe's own pride in his young nephew as he pointed the camera, she leaned forward and took it from the pile, away from the fire, then sat down. 'Right, tell me properly. What were you doing at Marjorie's and what's all this about manic cleaning?'

He shifted uncomfortably. 'I went to see Marjorie because I thought she might be able to tell me. She couldn't. Well, some of it, but not what matters.'

'Some of what?'

He drew a birthday card from down the side of the sofa. 'This is going on the fire too, but I'm saving it till the end. It's important. Without it I'd have remained deluded, possibly forever.'

He thrust it at her. She read it, wishing she'd found the right moment to talk about Suzanne Sherwell. It wouldn't have made the revelation any more palatable, but she would have been there to share it with him.

'So Joe had a wife and kids,' he said. 'He never told me. I had no idea.' He took the card from her and flicked it so it spun and glided down, causing the pile to slide into an untidy heap. 'Big deal, you might say. But then I find out they're estranged because he's done something unspeakable.

Though Marjorie doesn't know what it was, the Evil Deed. And even if she did, it seems they've all conspired down the years to keep me in the dark. For my own bloody good. You know what? Maybe they're right. So now his dog's gone I can put all this lot on the fire and that's it. He's not the man I thought he was so there's nothing to lose. Lost it already. New me, new life.'

Elin stared at the flames stirring behind the blackened glass of the stove. She felt Bede's eyes boring into her as if she were part of some conspiracy. Maybe she was.

'You're very quiet. What's up? Wishing you'd found out more about my sordid background before you accepted my hand in marriage?'

'Don't be ridiculous. Whatever Joe did, it doesn't affect the way I feel about you.'

She moved across to sit by him.

'Oh, Elin. Why can't things be back how they were?'

'They can be – between us, at least.'

They sat close for a while. He began to relax, then sat up, his face clouded again.

'This isn't working. Burning his things, his memory, him. I need to know.'

She reached out and hugged him to her. 'You've just said it yourself – it's all in the past.'

'But I know nothing about the past! My own father or the man who took his place. I feel like I don't even know who *I* really am.'

Elin took a deep breath. 'If it means that much to you, I think I know who you can ask.'

He drew away. 'What do you mean?'

'I had a visit a couple of weeks ago.' She looked at him uneasily. 'From Joe's wife.'

He stared at her, wide-eyed. 'What?'

'She'd only just found out he'd died. After a year and a half! I explained we didn't know about her. She said—'

'I don't care what the fuck she said, Elin. When were you thinking of telling me?'

'You were ill. The time wasn't right. I didn't think—'

'Didn't think? What else are you not saying? Just when I was beginning to come to terms with…with you being unfaithful. Your deceit. Whatever the bloody woman said, whatever she wants, I don't think I'll ever be able to trust *you* again!'

He stood, towering over her.

'I was all right on my own, managing perfectly well thank you, until he came along, showed me what a father could be, gave me something to believe in, all this. Even you – he was the one who brought us together. And just as I find out that the man I knew had been living some kind of lie, you turn round and reveal you've been hiding stuff from me – again! There's *no one* I can rely on, is there?'

He turned awkwardly and made his way towards the stairs.

'I'm back in our room now. You can have the spare bed. You'll forgive me if I don't sleep in his room myself, won't you?'

1st April, 2002

I saw it first on the news. An earth-mover at Calsthorpe Wood went out of control yesterday morning and nearly mowed down a number of protesters. One guy was badly hurt (I didn't know him, haven't seen any of them, only our Bede, since the Sophie incident), and it could have been a lot worse. They went crazy, so did the police. Turned into a riot. Battle stations. One way to get media attention, but not the kind of publicity they were wanting. There were a number of arrests and it'll be the end of that campaign – no one's going to get near the site from now on, security will be ramped up that much. I spent yesterday evening dreading a phone call from the police about our Bede, but it never came, thank goodness. He turned up this afternoon here at Alderleat. I doubt he'll be going back.

He swears he had nothing to do with it, he didn't go near that machine and anyway, he immobilises them, he'd never do anything that'd put anyone – on our side or theirs – in serious physical danger. As I'd expect, Grey and co are closing ranks against the authorities and Bede's fairly certain no one's going to name names – the Engineer or anyone else – but he's still up against a great big wall of hostility. Only Elin (they're very much an item now) seems to be sticking by him. I remembered those scenes back at the Calsthorpe community and asked him was it young Jack. He denied it of course, but he's a crap liar and it was damn obvious – I wasn't sure if he was protecting the kid or scared of Grey and Tig's anger if they thought he'd got their boy into trouble. Then again, he was so angry and hurt I was beginning to wonder what I could believe.

He said how it was killing him being blamed by his friends for something he didn't do. He almost wished he had done it – if it was his fault, at least he'd feel their outrage was justified. I told him no! You've done it, it's worse. You're still blamed, they're still mad at you but on top of that you've got the guilt to deal with. Believe me, I fucking know.

He looks at me, questioning, wanting me to say more and I almost did – the black, oozing guilt that eats away at your heart. Part of me feels I should have told him. I don't deserve his friendship any more than I deserved Suzie and the kids. Give him the truth, drive him away and let him go.

No way.

Time to move on

The next few days passed in a hostile silence broken only by an occasional exchange of words.

He spoke to her to point out that she'd hung her coat up on the wrong peg, that she hadn't put her shoes straight in the utility room, that she'd stacked the crockery wrongly in the cupboard. Ridiculous trifles, like an anchor to cling to as the bigger things got out of control.

He spoke to her to ask what Suzanne Sherwell had said, and to get her phone number, though as far as Elin knew, he'd not yet made any attempt to get in touch.

In his more forthcoming moods, he spoke to her of an all-pervading wrongness, about his stifling inability to go far, and the lack of freedom that weighed so heavily that he could hardly think straight.

Although Bede spent most of the time at the caravan or in the workshop making fixtures for it, or simply reading and scribbling notes, in the end Elin grew weary of the bleak black silences and the dark words. A group of conservation volunteers came to stay at Foxover Fields nature reserve. Her colleague was ill and she agreed to cover, staying in the warden's flat above the bunk barn – a first, since they lived so close and she usually cycled there on a daily basis. The group came for a few days then went, though Elin stayed on at the flat and spent more daytime hours in the shop than the rota called for.

She went home to Alderleat one lunch time to do her laundry, hoping she could have a reasonable conversation with Bede, lift the atmosphere and get back home. He was sitting at the desk staring at pages of notes and figures.

'Your leg,' she said in surprise. 'It's out of plaster.'

'Yeah.' He stayed with his back to her. 'Still using the crutches for now. Can't put too much weight on it too soon.'

'But your appointment's tomorrow. I was going to—'

'They phoned the other day. Cancellation.'

A wave of hurt washed through her. 'Why didn't you call me?'

He finally turned, his expression giving her nothing. 'Silvan was here when the call came. He offered to take me, said it'd save me having to hassle you. Sorry, didn't think it would bother you.'

He knew perfectly well how much the rejection would hurt her. As he turned back to the desk, she noticed the figures he was working on.

'Is that Sunny Days stuff?'

'Mm hm. Won't be for much longer.'

'What do you mean?'

'Couple of things I'd committed myself to. But once this is done, that's it. Time to move on.'

He picked up a ballpoint and started to write. Elin took the pen from his hands, snatched up the paper and turned it face down.

'Careful!' he snapped. 'You could've knocked my mug over.'

'I don't care! How long are you going to keep this up? I understand you've been upset, but can we please talk sensibly? Starting with you telling me what "time to move on" is supposed to mean.'

With a sigh, he swung the desk chair round to face her.

'I'm sure you can understand I don't want to work with Steve. As for the rest—'

‘What rest?’ The familiar shelves and books behind him seemed alien as a sense of dread descended.

‘Nothing stays the same. You know that as well as I do. Like the riverflow. There are peaceful times, but even then there’s the scratch, scratch, scratch of erosion. Imperceptible but…there. Until it’s time for big change, for renewal, and the floods come, taking away, yes, but bringing the promise of fertility and new beginnings in their wake. Just look outside. All this rain. Things are different. I feel like something’s going to give soon.’

‘What do you mean?’ Her voice was little more than a whisper.

He ran his hands through his hair, left them there. ‘Since you’ve been away, I’ve been thinking. A lot. You. Me. We need… Oh, El, let’s talk properly some time. Not… Give me a bit more time, hey?’

He turned back to the desk and started shuffling the papers.

‘How much bloody time do you need?’ She grabbed his shoulder and turned him back towards her. ‘If you’re trying to tell me it’s over, at least say it to my face!’

His eyes widened. ‘Of course not!’ He reached out to touch her. She caught his hand, lowered it and let go. ‘I’m sorry, El. That…that’s so far off the mark.’ He looked away. ‘Or is it wishful thinking? You’re the one who’s avoiding home. Do you want me to say it so you don’t have to?’

She refused to allow guilt in. ‘Avoiding home? Do you or do you not want time and space? Come on. At least tell me where this mark is that I’m missing so widely.’

He shook his head. ‘I don’t… Time and space, yes. I mean now, to get it right, but…more than that. For us. Maybe even getting away. Listen, I’ve been thinking about ways of…of rectifying things. Myself, my…our life. Can’t change anyone else. Even if we succeed in putting a stop to Northcote's bloody Prospect G, it's a drop in the ocean.' He waved his hand over the papers. 'See this? I may be irrational but I feel wrong switching on the computer right now. I can almost feel wasted energy and resources slipping away beneath my fingers. And all those connections creeping out into the vast, invisible network. That's what it's for, isn't it, to keep us connected, but…but with what? With a world I don't feel the slightest connection to. While all the time we're losing touch with what really matters.' He looked up at her and she saw the sleepless nights in his face. 'I feel like I've only just embarked on a journey; still haven't a clue where I'm going. The way we've been living our lives it's as though we're at the destination and intend to stay there till happy-ever-after. Well intentioned, but still wrong. I need to shed the mechanics of what I do. Things have got to give. I want… I…we…need to get away. We can. There's earth beyond Alderleat, trees beyond Holtwood, water beyond the leat and the Severn.'

'You mean, turn our backs on it all? Abandon all we've achieved?'

'See? Time and space. It's coming out wrong. Just for a while, maybe. And anyway I see it as building on what we've achieved. Taking it a step further. Give ourselves chance to really connect with the real world, with the trees, the earth, water, animals, birds. Everything that matters. Away from all the fucking hassle. I want so much for you to see where I'm coming from and share it with me…' He took a deep breath. 'Maybe not only the two of us. Maybe… Yes, I've been thinking about *that* as well…'

A momentary ray of hope lighted on her. She fought it. 'It doesn't work like that. You can't expect a child to come along and miraculously sort your head out.'

'But you… Together, we—'

'Yes, *together*, Bede. I haven't noticed much togetherness recently, have you? I don't know how much longer I can do this.'

Suppressing the urge to spill the dregs deliberately over his papers, she picked up his mug, turned abruptly and took it through to the kitchen. She turned in the doorway, willing him to make a move towards her. Was it disappointment, resentment…*hope*…she saw in his expression? He seemed to be struggling to find words. She had no energy to try and find them for him.

'You're right,' she said. 'I shouldn't rush you. You know where I am when you're ready.'

She put the washing on, gathered her things and left. When she returned later that afternoon to finish the laundry, she heard sounds of activity from the workshop, but it was locked and he didn't answer when she knocked. She didn't wait long.

Silvan called into the shop the following day; it was the first time she'd seen him since she'd come back from Fran's. The shop was quiet and she was alone. He brought a basket of assorted vegetables and salad to the counter.

'Long time no see.' He glanced at the basket. 'Tamsin's home some time tomorrow. I'm practising my cooking skills ready to treat her.'

Elin was reminded how much she'd look forward to seeing the girl after her holiday, though she wondered what on earth she'd say to her. She rang up Silvan's purchases, managing to keep her voice steady as she got the small talk out of the way. He told her how sorry he was about Kip, and she hoped he'd leave as soon as he was done. After paying, he leaned on the counter.

'You look stressed.'

She'd intended to say nothing, but he was provoking her. 'What did you say to Bede?'

'When?' He seemed taken aback by her tone of voice.

'Last week. Before I went away. When he pissed you off by saying you couldn't come and live at Alderleat. I seem to remember you telling me he was acting strangely.'

'Oh, that. I've apologised to him, Elin. I was a bit out of order.' He glanced around the empty shop. 'I've been meaning to ask you, to be honest. Something's wrong, isn't it? He called and asked me if I'd take him for his appointment. I'd have thought you'd have wanted to be there.'

Bede asked? He'd told her Silvan offered. 'Did he talk about anything in particular while you were with him?'

'Nothing much.' He spread his hands. 'At one point he was rambling about having a declutter. Out with the old, in with the new. Sounded deeper than he was letting on but I didn't push it.' Didn't push it? More like Bede wouldn't tell him; either way, Elin was surprised at her relief and how protective she felt towards her husband. 'Oh, I can't tell a lie,' he went on. 'He asked me not to say anything, but... He says you've walked out on him?'

'Walked out on him? I've been busy here and at the reserve.' No way was she going to say any more to Silvan.

'I know things haven't been easy since his accident. I'm sorry if anything I've said made things worse. I can imagine what you're going through.'

'That's unlikely.'

'But you shouldn't take his behaviour to heart. He hasn't been right recently, you know it yourself. I mean...all that with your dog.' He looked at her, eyes full of concerned apology. 'He needs help, not blame. That's why I tried to hold my tongue when we found Kip. But Tammy told me the way he'd been and I saw him the afternoon before it happened. I'm sorry, Elin.'

She stood thinking about Bede's state of mind, wishing she'd swallowed her pride and either broached the subject of a counsellor or talked to someone herself, and wondering whether there was a grain of truth in what Silvan was implying about the dog. Bede had hinted as much himself. The bell over the door rang out, echoing her jangling nerves. A small group of people came in and she managed to get Silvan to leave as she composed herself for her customers.

After she closed the shop, the remaining hours of the day stretched emptily ahead of her and she went back home – to Alderleat – for her guitar, some CDs, and basket weaving gear. She got out of the car and stood for a moment, steeling herself. Heavy clouds covered half the sky, threatening from a distance. A small, white clump hung down, wispy drifts like udders reaching towards the ground. As if it would start raining milk – something else gone wrong. The workshop was silent and her heart sank as she wondered if he'd barricaded himself in again. The very thought made her want to march in and tackle him, to stay until they'd got things straight, once and for all. Part of her, the weary part, just wanted to go in and collect her stuff.

To her surprise, the kitchen door was unlocked. As soon as she walked in she sensed there was no one there, but she called him all the same. She gathered her things and took them out to the car. Glancing up at the bridge over the leat, the field, and the caravan beyond, she had the same sense of emptiness. She had no idea how far he could walk by now – the realisation saddened her – but she knew how caged he'd been feeling for weeks. She'd seen Frank Barnham the day before. 'Your Bede out and about again?

I saw him on the Holtwood path earlier. I was sorry to hear about your dog, by the way.'

She went back inside for her guitar. She'd been so absorbed she hadn't noticed: there was a blank space on the wall where their wedding photo, then Joe's portrait, had been. In the living room, she saw that the pile of Joe's things by the fire had gone, and wondered emptily if their photo had joined them in the flames. Then she saw it, laid on the little table by Bede's usual place. Face up, as though he'd been looking at it. A lump came to her throat. The tears spilled; she sat down on the sofa and gave in. It happened almost every night, but it felt different, more biting, in her own home. They'd come through so much – why now? What had happened to them? If only they could talk properly. She sat listening for the sound of footsteps, the door opening and closing. Sounds that never came.

After a while, she told herself to be strong and got up. If he was able to go out for walks, his mood might change. She left him a note.

Didn't want you to think there's been an intruder and start worrying.
I just came to pick up my guitar and a few bits.

She thought long and hard before signing it,

Love, Elin x

Let him be the first to deny love.

His fingers tightened around the smooth wood. He'd seen the thumb stick at Halbury show one year and Elin had bought it for him because it felt as though he and the wood belonged together. One day he wanted to learn how to shape and adapt a stick so perfectly. He loved the way it nestled against his hand, like an extension of his arm, but he'd never thought he'd truly need it. Not for a few decades yet.

He leaned on the staff like an old friend, so much more a soulmate than the harsh, rattling metal crutches he'd left lying in the bedroom. Relishing the support and wishing it could also lend him stamina, he marvelled at how unfit it was possible to get in the space of a few short weeks. He paused for breath on the crest of a rise and saw Alderleat small below him. The car was just leaving. He wished Elin hadn't let him drive her away. He wanted her help to untangle the muddle of his thoughts, needed her to make him feel right, like the stick made him feel right, like being here immersed in the whispering of the evening breeze through the ragged grass made him feel right. To wrap him up and comfort him with her lies.

That was where it led to; was he only learning now? The kind of wisdom that came with life, not a venerable saint's name. They all came at you with secrets, lies and deceit, ready to well up and overwhelm you like the waters of the river suddenly rose up in spate, to carry you along and dash you against some obstacle. You had to prepare your defences. Just as the flood brought new silt and fertility, the lies and deceit brought renewed strength. Flush it out, wash it away, start anew.

Dusk was beginning to gather with the clouds but it would be a while before the lights of Foxover and the villages beyond came on to spread their fire across the valley floor and the hillside, like the flames of the woodburner that had removed all trace of Joe, giving no answers but burning away all desire for them. Who needed to know? Not him, not any more.

The car, so small, slowed for the Holtwood corner before heading for the bridge. Let her go. Let her wonder where he was. The wind was his companion tonight, the wind that could whip up a storm or fan a blaze, tugging at his coat, making a streaming pennant of his hair, filling his ears and his thoughts like the distant river. The meaning borne by the water and the wind still lay just out of reach, but it was beautiful, like a haunting song sung in a foreign language. Who needed words? The feeling was there, its precision just beyond his grasp – but if he didn't fully understand, then it couldn't lie.

Yesterday had been a tentative experiment. He'd walked as far as Holtwood and been pleased with how well his leg could carry him. Tonight he had a sense of purpose and he could stay out all night if he had to. That wouldn't be wise – and wasn't he beginning to know wisdom now; the wisdom of trusting no one but himself – but he could if he had to. Freedom.

The wind, prickly with a hint of rain, stirred the grass around him like the ever-widening circles of freedom. His eye drawn to the rippling green and yellow waves, he only just managed to stop himself from calling out to Kip.

Elin was comforted by playing her guitar. She shouldn't have left it so long. Her fingers found their patterns, frustrated and halting at first, then settling and soothing. She played her river song, the one she loved, Bede loved, the one that seemed to strike such a chord at the Horseshoes music nights. She faltered, her thoughts wandering. All Bede's talk of change and time to move on. Surely he couldn't really be suggesting they left Alderleat? If even the smallest part of the recent chain of events had been down to Philip Northcote, there was no way they could give in and let the man win. Even this gulf between them was conceding a kind of victory to him. She stared across at the black-and-white photos of the nature reserve on the walls, sighed and began to play again.

She woke in the night. It was as though something at the edge of her consciousness had stirred her. Maybe from outside, maybe from within a dream.

The window in the gable of the two-room flat above the bunk barn was deeply recessed and she could see surprisingly little. The Foxover Fields building stood on a rise on the edge of the village, out of reach of the highest-ever floods. Her eye was drawn to a redness on the edge of her vision, but she couldn't see more without going downstairs and outside. Her sleep-fogged mind told her it was simply the orange glow-fires of the street lamps that Bede talked about sometimes – simple light pollution picked out and swollen by changeable weather and river mist.

Still the same hands

Rain pattered in trickling waves on the window as he woke and reached for the painkillers. The inevitable headache had become routine, but he felt invigorated this morning. With the special quality of the outside night air still close, as though he could reach out and hold it to him, he got up early, feeling more himself than he had for ages. There was some way still to go, but it was a green lane he was travelling instead of sitting staring at a map without his glasses.

After a shower, he made his way downstairs. As he sat at the table with a mug of coffee and bowl of muesli, he picked up his glasses from next to the phone and told himself to stop feeling relieved whenever things were as they should be. To feel such relief was to acknowledge that things still weren't truly normal, and he wanted the crutch of normality. He reached for the note Elin left last night. Her writing tugged at his heart – *Love, Elin* – but he breathed deeply and put it to one side, face down. He unfolded the other paper she'd given him, the one with the details, and set it out in front of him, noting that the writing was the same as the *Return to Sender* on Niall's birthday card envelope.

A glance at his watch, quarter to seven, told him it was too early. He put the paper and the phone next to each other in readiness and grabbed the crutches. A twinge of wrongness nagged him at the feel of cold metal and plastic, but they were to hand and he had things on his mind other than trying to remember where he'd left his walking stick.

He crossed the rain-soaked yard to spend an hour or two in the workshop.

At half past eight he considered it reasonable to make the call. Without putting the kettle on, without washing up his breakfast things, without doing anything that would dilute his resolve, he sat down at the kitchen table, picked the phone up and dialled.

A self-assured woman's voice answered.

'Suzanne?' He introduced himself.

'I'd almost given up on you,' she said coldly. 'I was thinking of trying again myself. Didn't your wife pass the message on?'

'Not straight away. Anyway, she has now and there are things I'd like to talk to you about.' He hesitated.

'Sure. Would you like to meet later this week? Tomorrow, even?'

'No, no. I mean now. On the phone.'

'I'd prefer to meet,' she insisted. 'I want to see the papers before agreeing to anything.'

'What papers?'

'Joe's will, for a start.'

'Oh, for God's sake. Yeah, all right. We can meet up about that. Though it's been…a difficult time. We haven't had much chance to think about it or consult anyone. I've also got something else I should let you have. A bit late,' he laughed drily, 'but better late than never, hey? An eighteenth birthday card for Niall. From Dad. I was going to put it on the fire, but…I didn't. So you might as well have it to pass on to him.'

'What do you know about him?' She sounded worried, the first hint of emotion he'd detected in her voice. 'Have you seen him?'

'Never clapped eyes on him. I know sweet FA about him,

sorry. But I thought you might like the card. I've had enough of burning stuff. Overrated. Now, there are things I'd like to ask you, too. And, unlike me, I think you do know the answers.'

He tensed, steeling himself.

'I can guess what you're referring to. I'm sorry, I said more than I should have to your wife. I'd rather talk to you in person – with her, maybe? It's not the kind of thing I'd be comfortable telling you over the phone.'

Not this woman as well. Silence, lies, conspiracy. His hand tightened into a fist. 'Why not?'

'I'm only thinking it might be better for you—'

'Listen!' He banged his fist down on the table. 'You don't know me, you don't know what my feelings are or how to fucking spare them!'

'Don't you shout at me.'

'I'm not f— I'm sorry, I didn't mean to… Will you just tell me why Joe left?'

'Nothing like getting straight to the point.'

'Please. Suzanne. *Aunt* Suzanne!'

There was a long silence. His index finger was entangled in a strand of hair, winding it round and round, like the old-fashioned telephone cord the first time he'd phoned Joe. And later, Elin. A nervous wreck then, too.

'Oh, what the heck. Don't blame me if you don't like what you hear. Very well, I told your uncle, my husband, never to darken our door again because I couldn't trust him. Because he confessed to me that he…he'd murdered a man. And from the state of him, he was obviously telling the truth.'

'Murdered?' He blinked at the unexpected.

'Yes, murdered. Thinking about it later I understood he was seriously provoked – but he had a temper, as you probably know, and I couldn't be sure he wouldn't resort to violence again.'

'What happened?' Bede stared at the hair wound round his finger like a hangman's noose.

'He…he must have been really close to his sister. Your mother. Though you'd probably find that hard to believe. I don't think they saw each other after—'

'Not that I knew of.' He tapped the phone handset impatiently. 'Go on.'

'She…she was raped when she was seventeen. After a disco, party, whatever. It seems she knew the bastard by sight. So did Joe. When he found out, he lost it. Tracked him down, and… Maybe he only intended to beat him up, teach him a lesson, who knows? When the lad's body was found in the river – drowned, bloated, barely identifiable – they put it down to a mugging, never found the culprit. Joe said that Lydia knew, of course, but whatever else, she wasn't going to see her brother tried and banged up for murder.'

Bede closed his eyes, enveloping himself in the swirling, mottled semi-darkness of his eyelids.

'And before you ask, no, Joe didn't tell me who it was. It wasn't important to me. I'd never even met his sister. What mattered to me was I didn't want that man near me. Didn't want him having anything to do with my kids. He'd been a good enough father, though he was prone to the occasional outburst, but after he confessed, I was scared. What might provoke him to do it again? He wasn't the man I'd known. Can you understand that?'

He nodded, opening his eyes. He yanked his finger roughly from the tangle of hair to make himself feel.

'Hello? Are you still there? I'm sorry, I didn't want to tell you like that. You're right, I don't know you, but no one deserves—'

'It's OK.'

'I'm sure you could find out about your father properly if you wanted. It would have been in the local paper at the time, you can search the archives. He might turn out to have been a decent enough young man in other respects. Made a mistake, may have regretted it. Then again—'

'*I said it's OK!*'

He imagined her taking a step back, relieved she hadn't done this face-to-face after all.

'Yes, well. I know it must be hard. I'll leave you in peace. Just…can you remember Joe saying anything about Niall? Our son?'

'Nothing. Only the stupid card.'

'I haven't heard from him for over three years. Reported him missing, but there's been no trace. I was worried about our Niall before, but… If Joe contacted him…'

'He obviously didn't. The envelope was with it. Returned unopened. As you know.'

'That wasn't the only time he tried. Please let me know if you hear anything.'

He heard himself saying he was sure there was nothing to worry about, coming out with some platitude about unpredictable young lads. After he put the phone down without properly thanking her, without properly saying goodbye, he realised they'd never arranged to meet up after all.

His hands lay in front of him on the table. Rapist. Murderer. They were still the same hands. Why were people so afraid of telling? Why the secrets and lies? Still the same hands. A huge wave of love washed over him for his mum, who'd kept him with her – let him live, if he thought about it – and loved him despite who he was, what he represented.

He got up to go to the workshop, immerse himself in

activity. Remembering the drenching he'd got earlier, merely crossing the yard, he grabbed his coat. It smelled strongly of smoke. He paused with it half-on, and realised it wasn't his usual jacket. This one was irredeemably worn out, saved to wear for the dirtiest of jobs; he'd forgotten it was still there. One pocket felt slightly heavy; he thrust his hand in and felt something metallic. He frowned and replaced the key on its designated hook, then hung the tattered old coat back on its proper peg. As he tugged on his summer-weight waterproof, hood up against the rain, he hoped fervently that he'd soon conquer this fog of absent-mindedness.

Carole came into the shop, flapping her umbrella open and shut in the doorway to shake off the raindrops. Elin was glad of the way the rota had fallen. It was hard to keep a cheerful face on things, and it would be good to have her friend around. She might even steel herself to talk things through.

'Sorry I'm late.' Carole walked briskly to the counter. 'Isn't it awful?'

'What?' Elin wasn't sure if she could face more bad news.

'Haven't you heard? Oh, I forgot you're still staying at Foxover Fields.' A mixture of pity and reproach flitted across her face. 'You wouldn't have come in past Bridge Farm, would you? There's been a fire. Pretty bad, as far as I could see. It's cordoned off of course, but I spoke to one of the fire crew.'

'Oh.' Elin gripped the edge of the counter. 'Was anyone hurt?'

'I'm afraid Marjorie's been taken to hospital. The effects

of smoke. I heard she may have had a stroke. Philip wasn't there, lucky bastard – he was at Kate's last night, as far as I know.' She smiled grimly. 'The village's worst-kept secret definitely a secret no more. Though I doubt they'll mind under the circumstances. God, Elin, the place looks awful.'

'I can't believe it. You know, I think I saw something in the middle of the night. I was half-asleep.'

'They're not committing themselves yet, but I heard it started with an explosion in an old central heating boiler.'

'We've been trying for ages to get her to replace it.'

'There's a rumour it was tampered with. Arson. It's amazing how they know. Mind you, the firemen and police have been combing the place since the small hours.'

The bell over the door went.

'You go and put the kettle on,' Carole said quietly, as if sensing that Elin couldn't face talking to anyone.

She made their coffees in a daze, vaguely aware of a number of people coming and going. Nothing like a crisis to create a hum of activity.

'Here she is now,' she heard Carole saying as she took the mugs through.

Elin recognised the detective who'd led the investigation into Bede's accident. Hughes, wasn't it? He shook her hand. She beckoned him through to the staff room, throwing Carole an apologetic glance as she went.

'I understand Mrs Denman's told you about the fire,' he began.

Elin asked him about Marjorie. He knew no more than Carole had told her, but said he'd keep this as brief as possible so she could phone the hospital and find out. He asked if she'd seen anything and she mentioned the glimpse she'd had when she woke briefly.

'You weren't at home last night?'

She felt he was watching her intently as she muttered something about having work to catch up on at the Foxover Fields office and staying over as it got so late.

'How's your husband doing after that accident? Last time I saw you, you were worried about leaving him. He must be recovering well.'

'Oh yes, he's been quite capable of looking after himself for a while now. He's still using crutches, though.' She stopped short of *as far as I know*; the distance between them was still something she hated to admit. 'But the cast's off his leg and he's more mobile every day.'

'I'm glad to hear it.' He sat back with a frown. 'Mr Northcote tells me your husband was at his mother's house a few weeks ago. Repairing the boiler where it's believed the fire started. Mr Northcote also believes you hold a key to her house.'

There was no denying either claim. 'We... Marjorie gave us a spare key long before Philip came back to live in Foxover. In case anything happened...'

She was beginning to wish they'd given it back.

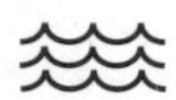

The knocking was loud, almost hammering.

'Come in.'

Bede remembered he'd locked the door. Cursing the interruption, he reached for the crutches and went to open up. He vaguely recognised the man in the doorway.

Detective Inspector Hughes introduced himself. Ah yes, the guy who'd got nowhere tracing the cause of his accident. Hughes peered into the workshop, but Bede stayed resolutely on the threshold, his weight on his right leg, stepping back only enough to allow the man to shelter from the worst of the rain. Never let it be said he was entirely inconsiderate.

'I'm investigating the fire at Bridge Farm, Mr Sherwell. Can I ask you a few questions?'

Bede frowned. 'Bridge Farm? What kind of fire?' The detective looked at him as if to say, the hot kind, with flames and smoke. 'I mean, what's happened?'

Hughes glanced at the crutches. 'Would you like to go somewhere a bit more comfortable to talk?'

'I'm fine, but if it suits you.'

After a quick look round to make sure everything was safe to leave, he secured the workshop and led the way across the yard. He felt under scrutiny as he unlocked the kitchen door, then waved a hand at a chair by the table.

'It's good to see you're security conscious,' the detective remarked as he sat down. 'A lot of people who live in the country can be a bit careless.'

Bede shrugged. 'Tell me about this fire at Bridge Farm.'

'It was quite a blaze, around midnight.' He looked at him intently. 'You hadn't heard?'

'Haven't been anywhere or seen anyone this morning. How bad is it? Is Marjorie OK? Marjorie Northcote?'

As he listened to the news that his old friend was in hospital, he stared at his feet, full of regret for the anger he'd been feeling. It wasn't her fault that she'd kept Joe's secrets for him.

'Mr Sherwell?'

He looked up.

'I asked where you were, what you were doing, last night.'

'What? Me? I was here.'

'At home? All evening?'

Bede sighed, ran a hand through his hair. 'Yes. No. What

can I say? I went for a walk. I like going for walks. Especially when I'm stressed. I haven't been able to get out much recently. It did me good.'

He turned away, looked out of the window, watching the raindrops patterning a puddle on the yard.

'Did you see anything?'

He shook his head.

'Did anyone see you?'

'Not that I know of.'

Bede sat forward as he realised where this was heading. Apart from the circumstantial evidence of his ongoing feud with Philip, culminating in his upset about the death of his dog, there was the question of Marjorie's spare key and his knowledge of the ancient central heating boiler. Wet footsteps in the boiler room between the two houses had been interspersed with singular prints made by the rubber tips of a set of crutches; Inspector Hughes found that the boot prints matched an old pair here in the Alderleat utility room. Bede's protests as he gestured towards the ones on his feet and insisted that he hadn't been wearing them were less compelling than the bald fact that they were damp.

As was the smoke-smelling jacket. 'I suppose you weren't wearing this, either?'

He shook his head again in silence. Hughes indicated his mobile, lying in its usual place on the windowsill.

'What's your number?'

Mystified, Bede recited it. The detective consulted his notebook.

'Can I have a look?'

'Be my guest. I haven't touched it for a couple of days, though.'

The detective pulled on a pair of latex gloves and

unplugged it from the charger. After a few taps, he showed Bede a text, sent to Northcote P at 00:26 that morning.

> Now you know what it feels like to have a place that matters to you destroyed.

A rising panic threatened to engulf him. 'I don't even know Northcote's number! What's it doing on my phone?'

There was a sense of inevitability, of events spiralling out of control, as he agreed – as if he had any choice – to go to the police station to give a statement. A statement he knew would not be believed.

The news from the hospital was better than Elin had feared. It seemed that Marjorie was stable, though the chances of her going home any time soon were slim. That would leave plenty of time to repair the house, Elin thought grimly. The detective would have spoken to Bede by now and she wanted to be with him. She went through to the shop and was about to ask Carole if she could spare her for a few minutes, when she heard Silvan's voice. Her heart sank.

'It seems we're honoured to have the company of the hero of the hour,' Carole announced.

'Hardly,' he protested. 'I only did what anyone would've done.'

'Which is?' Elin said.

'First things first,' Carole said. 'What did they tell you at the hospital?'

Elin gave them her news and asked his.

'I fell asleep in front of the telly last night. I was on my way to bed when I looked out the window and noticed the fire. I called 999 then dashed out. So I rocked up and saw a blaze coming from the lobby between the two houses – you know, the old lady's place, Mrs Northcote's, and Philip's. The smoke was choking me before I could get near to see more.' He scratched his nose as if the acrid fumes were still irritating his nostrils. 'I saw Philip's car wasn't there. I couldn't have got closer if I'd wanted to but I assumed he was safe. Then, shit, I only saw smoke drifting out from Mrs Northcote's kitchen, didn't I? I was working my way round, trying to find a way in to see if she was OK, when the firemen arrived and broke the door down to rescue her.' He glanced at Carole. 'Hardly heroic but I tried. I don't mind telling you I was terrified.'

Elin felt guilty that she'd not seen the blaze, but consoled herself that it would have been the fire engine or police that had woken her and so there was nothing useful she could have done.

'So I haven't slept a wink since. There's nothing doing at the shoot today, of course, so I'm just on my way back to catch up on some kip. I'm only being nosy really, forgive me, but I thought I saw Bede just now, heading somewhere in the back of a car.'

'What car?' Elin said sharply.

'Blue one. The driver might have been someone I recognised from last night. Couldn't tell. It was all blurry with the rain.'

'Inspector Hughes had a blue car,' Carole said helpfully.

'So what d'you think that's about?'

Something inside Elin snapped. 'I've been here all morning, Silvan. Bede's been at Alderleat. So I really have no idea.'

I wasn't there

The rainstorm made the day dull and lights were on, the house pulsing to the beat of loud rock music. Tamsin knocked and waited. No way Elin would hear it in her cocoon of sound. She stepped into the kitchen and called. The roar of a vacuum cleaner competed with the music. She went through to the living room and called again.

Elin jumped and turned as if vacuuming were a crime. Flashing Tamsin a strained smile, she hurried over to the old-fashioned music centre and killed the sound.

'You're back. Did you have a good time in Italy?'

'Yeah, great, thanks. I've brought some pics on my phone to show you. But how are you? Shit, I can't believe what's been happening. I wanted to come round yesterday, but it was too late by the time we got back.'

'I'd probably have been up.' She laughed thinly. 'What have you heard? Sorry, sit down. I can spare a few minutes, but I've got to tidy up.'

'Sure. I'll give you a hand.'

'Thanks.' Elin was gazing across the room. She hadn't looked at Tamsin once since she arrived. It wasn't like her. 'Bede's coming home soon.'

'Coming home? He's in the clear? I couldn't believe it, honestly, Elin. I'm sick of Philip and his paranoia. I mean, I know his mum's ill because of it, and I'm so sorry about that. But she's your friend too, isn't she? There's no way Bede would do anything like that. That's why I'm here – so you can tell me the real story. Have they let him off?'

‘No. Bail. With curfew conditions and one of those electronic tags.’

‘Wow. He’ll probably take it apart and start working out how to hack it.’

Elin’s expression made her wish she could take it back. ‘It’s serious, Tamsin.’

‘Yeah, sorry.’

Elin bent to unplug the vacuum cleaner. ‘All the evidence points to Bede and he…he hasn’t been himself.’ She flopped against the wall, looking desolate. ‘As you saw. Though I can’t believe he’d do a thing like that and he swears blind he had nothing to do with it. When he bothers speaking at all. I wish I could get through to him.’

‘I’m so sorry. I’ve been awake all night thinking about it – about when we were working on the caravan together while you were up north. He was behaving weirdly. I should’ve noticed, done more.’

‘You?’ Elin laughed incredulously.

Tamsin felt wounded. ‘People say I’m a good listener, you know.’

‘I don’t mean that. Sorry. I’m sure you are. But you haven’t been married to him for the last fifteen years. I’m the one should have seen, should have done something. He gave me enough signs, for God’s sake. And I just took the huff and left.’

‘I’m sure it wasn’t like that.’

Elin busied herself winding away the vacuum cleaner cable. ‘I *wasn’t there.*’

Her tears spilled over. Tamsin touched her arm. Elin brushed her away and fetched a tissue from a box on the bookshelf across the room.

‘Could you put the hoover away for me, please? Under the stairs.’

As she returned to the kitchen, Tamsin heard a clatter and Elin cursing.

'God knows what this is doing here. Could you put it in the stand by the front door, please?'

She handed her a walking stick.

'That's nice.' Tamsin examined it; the smooth loop at the top fitted her hand perfectly, though it was made for someone taller.

'Bede fell in love with it at Halbury show and I bought it for him.' Elin's face clouded. 'I'm surprised it hasn't gone on the fire like everything else.'

'Too useful,' Tamsin said, trying to defuse the atmosphere. 'More his image than the crutches.'

'He obviously thought the same. There's mud on it, look. Idiot. If he damages his wrist or his ankle because he's not following medical advice, we'll just be back to square one.' She shook her head. 'No, we won't. We'll never be back to anything.'

This time she allowed Tamsin to hug her as a stray sob escaped her. It was scary to see cracks appearing in this woman who usually took everything in her stride. Elin's world had become part of Tamsin's and the cracks were beneath her feet, too.

When the time came for Elin to go and collect Bede, Tamsin got a lift to the village. As they crossed the bridge, she looked at the swollen river not far below and the submerged fields to either side. It had been dark when they crossed on their way home the night before, and Tamsin hadn't noticed how high the water level had become.

'It won't be long now,' Elin said. 'We're going to be flooded again. Not so long since last time.'

'It might not happen.'

'It will. Now it's got this high, and rising. It's still raining, probably more so up in the mountains.' She sighed. 'They'll be busy moving stuff in the shop. I feel bad that I can't help.'

She had to get Bede home. As Tamsin listened to her saying how the village would probably be off-limits to him but they were lucky he could come home at all, it became clear to her how bad things were. Arson, attempted manslaughter, attempted murder, even. She thought back about the warnings – her mother's, which she'd brushed off, and Silvan's, which she'd scoffed at as teasing – and the way she never quite knew how to take Bede. Yet she admired Elin's loyalty.

'Do you want me to go and ask if they want a hand at the shop?' Tamsin said as she got out of the car.

Elin managed a smile. 'Thanks. I'm sure they'd appreciate any offer of help.'

'Shall I come and see you later? Moral support?'

'If you don't mind getting your head bitten off.' Elin smiled wistfully, paused for a moment longer, then drove off.

Before she reached the Foxover Storehouse, Tamsin felt her phone buzz and stopped to read a text.

Can't wait till tonight, bae. I can take a short break in about ½ hr. See u at mine? S x

Glancing guiltily between the shop ahead of her and the raging river behind, she decided that an hour or so wouldn't make much difference. Better to wait at Silvan's, catch up with him first, then go along to the shop afterwards.

It was only the second time she'd been to the gamekeepers' scruffy house on the edge of the village. One of his housemates let her in.

'He's not back yet. Go on up if you like.'

He gave her a knowing look; she prided herself in meeting the older boy's eye nonchalantly, feeling how much she'd grown up over the last few weeks.

Silvan's attic room was as much of a mess as she remembered. Her room at home was better than this – bigger, brighter and cosier – but she wished he'd ask her here more often. She'd do anything to get away from her mum, her brother Simon, and now Philip. Stepping over strewn items of clothing on the floor, she made her way over to the window. There was a clear view of Bridge Farm. At first glance it looked untouched, until she saw the black ghosts of smoke staining the walls around a couple of windows. With a slight shiver, she imagined Silvan getting up, seeing the glow and rushing out. Just her luck to miss out on the excitement – why did she always manage to be away at the wrong time? She looked at her watch. Not long now before he'd be here to tell her about it in person.

She gathered some half-empty mugs together to take down to the kitchen. Shaking her head, she took his guitar from where it lay across the tatty sofa and set it on its stand, then bent to pick up an ashtray. As she straightened, she noticed a battered notebook sticking out from under a cushion. Another glance at her watch told her she had a few minutes. It might be where he jotted down his songs – she didn't always get his lyrics, but she might catch a glimpse of an out-of-character love song, or… Boys didn't usually keep diaries, but Silvan was different. It would be cool if he'd written something about her.

Carefully noting where she'd taken it from, she sat down and opened a random page.

Her breath caught. The handwriting struck her before a single word registered. This wasn't Silvan's spidery writing.

This was Joe Sherwell's. She flicked through and it fell open at a page marked by a No Surrender gig flyer.

10 September, 2001

I love some of the things our Bede comes out with. This evening we were up above the house looking at the weird orange glow in the sky. 'They should learn to love the darkness,' he says. 'As long as there's enough sunlight by day, enough light indoors to see by, darkness itself isn't a threat. Don't you agree?' And he waves his arm out over the landscape. 'Lighting the darkness not only gives them a false sense of security, but creates a deeper shadow beyond. So they tame that shadow with more light. Where will it end?'

And he looks at me as if he's said something embarrassing. I nod, encouraging like, and he starts talking about how he used to imagine the streetlights as big cleansing fires across the hillsides of his childhood, scary and inescapable. It's times when he opens up like that when I realise how close we've become.

The words *our Bede* and *how close we've become* had been underlined in blue biro and a belligerent circle surrounded *big cleansing fires*. Catching her breath, Tamsin glanced towards the window then flicked through to a page near the back that also fell open, similarly scrawled over.

So the tractor's on the road at last. Never thought he'd do it. That showed me, didn't it? Showed them, showed all those who think we're hiding away doing nothing! Watch out, gas guzzlers!

Three additional blue biro exclamation marks had been added in the margin.

It's been such a beautiful day. Not just the weather – we're more than that. The three of us – I can't express how much they mean to me. How lucky I am. Since they got married and came to live here, none of the rest of it, none of them, matter any more.

'Oh, don't they?' the blue biro pronounced in Silvan's writing.

I tried to get in touch with our Niall recently but he doesn't want to know. Like our Emma didn't. And I'm amazed to find I don't care any more. Sod 'em. I have a new family now. And who knows, one day there may be more. Grandchildren – well, grand-nephews and nieces. Never thought I'd be bothered about that, but I heard them arguing about starting a family and it got to me. I'll have to have a word with our Bede. It sounded serious. I don't want something like that to come between them. Us. Not now. The thought of a new life, chance for a new beginning thrills me, but I know we can be perfectly happy just the three of us, too. We'll get through it either way. We've achieved so much together, and there's so much more we can do.

The river's rising and I fear there are floods on the way, but that won't stop us.

Our next

The sound of footsteps on the stairs threw her into a panic. She shoved the diary back where it came from and sat trying to look casual as the door opened.

'Tammy!' Silvan paused, looking her up and down. 'You're early.'

She tried to nudge the book further beneath the cushion with her leg as she stood. 'I was in the village – thought I'd surprise you,' she said. 'Did Liam tell you I'd arrived?'

'Yeah. I've missed you.' He grabbed hold of her and kissed her hard, then stepped back and studied her. 'You're looking good. Beautifully tanned. You've obviously had better weather than here.'

She smiled. 'It's been good. As good as it could be without you.'

His eyes slid past her to the sofa. 'Have you been waiting long?'

'Not really. I was just looking out at Bridge Farm. Thinking about what happened.'

'Were you?' He moved to perch on the sofa, head cocked insolently up at her. 'From here?'

'No. No, of course not. A few minutes ago, I mean. Go on, tell me all about it.'

He got up and wandered over to the window as if sight of the house would help the story. He turned suddenly.

'You looked guilty as hell when I came in.'

Her eyes flicked down to the side before meeting his. 'I wasn't sure… Liam said come up, but I didn't know if you'd mind me being here.'

'Mind?' He glanced down to where she'd just looked. 'Why should I mind?'

He stepped towards her and gripped her arms tightly.

'You're hurting me, Silvan.'

'What were you doing?'

He gave her a brief shake to emphasise his words. She jolted against the sofa and the book fell to the floor. They both stared at it.

'Did you read it?'

'I... No.' Her voice caught in her throat.

Holding her wrist vice-like with one hand, Silvan leaned forward and picked up the diary with the other. 'Don't lie to me, Tamsin. You know what this is, don't you?'

She swallowed, shaking her head without speaking. He put the book down on the sofa and grabbed her other arm.

'So why try and hide it?' he demanded, shaking her again.

'Stop it!' He continued to glare at her. 'Please, Silvan, let me go. I...I don't know anything about it.' She struggled but knew she was no match for him physically. She searched his face, trying to find the warmth in his dark eyes that had first captivated her. 'Honest, I was...I was just being nosy. What's the big deal, anyway?'

She moved to touch his face, distract him. He turned away. 'Don't try it on. You saw it, didn't you?'

'So it's a diary. Looks like it could be Joe Sherwell's.'

'Full of lies!'

His intensity scared her.

'So what?' she said quickly. 'I never even knew him. Did you? How come you've got it? Why—' She was dying to know why Silvan had made those notes in it, but the look on his face silenced her.

'Me?' He raised his eyebrows. 'You've been away, Tammy, you don't know how bad things have got.' He sighed and the tension ebbed a little. 'Sorry, I over-reacted a bit. Bede's flipped. He...he was burning some old stuff so I took the liberty of rescuing this plus a few other bits. He's a mate, you know, despite everything, and I thought he might regret it later.'

'Does he know you took it?'

He gave her a hard stare. 'Got bigger things on his mind

now, hasn't he? Seems like it's not the only burning he's been up to.'

'You don't know that was him.'

He laughed harshly. 'Trust you to take his side. There's enough evidence. They're questioning him now, so I believe.'

She looked away from the cold gleam in his eyes. 'What's the diary got to do with it?'

'Nothing. Except maybe he was going to burn that, too.'

He laughed. She forced a smile as he drew her towards him. She wanted him to be telling the truth. For it to be all right. She pretended it was as he released her arms and ran his hands through her hair. She drew away, reached down and quickly picked up the notebook.

'I think we ought to, like, give this to Elin to look after.'

'Don't be stupid. Give it back, Tamsin.'

She had no idea what it was about, but he was scaring her. She clutched it tighter.

'Look, I've got to go. See you.'

He lunged at her; she dodged and ran for the door. She tripped halfway down the stairs. The floor came up to meet her in a hollow swoop before she managed to grab the banister. She hung for a moment, steadying herself, as footsteps thumped down behind her.

'Tammy! Wait! It's not what you think. Come back and let me tell you about it.'

Doubting he was going to tell her anything she wouldn't rather hear from Elin, she fumbled with the Yale lock, wrenched the door open, tumbled out and slammed it closed behind her.

She dashed from the house, heading for the high street. A strap on her sandal had broken when she fell; she stumbled slightly as she ran, but reached the junction.

Across the road, the door of the pub beckoned. Two cars passed, the time they took magnified by the sound of Silvan's feet getting horribly close. She finally made an impatient dash towards the entrance of the pub car park. Brakes screeched and a horn sounded. She hadn't seen the car pulling in. Her sandal gave way again; she fell and the book flew from her hand. Silvan dashed past her and picked it up.

'Give me that!' she yelled.

Scrambling to her feet, she saw Brian getting out of his car, obviously shaken. 'Is everything all right?'

'It's OK, mate,' Silvan said calmly. 'I'm trying to explain to her. I'd written something in my notebook here that I shouldn't have. I've apologised but she just won't have it. Come on now, Tammy, you're showing us both up.'

She shook her head. Tears of shock and frustration soaked her face. 'Give me that book!'

'It's not important. See? This is how unimportant it is.'

He strode across the beer garden where the river was lapping dangerously close. Brian looked at Tamsin in confusion. Silvan reached the fence and hurled the diary into the churning grey water.

In memory

A huge globule of rain exploded onto the windscreen. Another followed, then a spatter of them. Elin thought she saw a flicker as she turned the wipers on.

'Was that lightning?' she asked.

'Didn't notice. Probably.'

She was concentrating on the road ahead, but could sense Bede's unmoving presence beside her. He was hunched in his seat, staring out of the side window. He'd hardly said a word.

'I've been thinking about Halbury show. It's in a couple of weeks' time. You remember that really sunny one, three years ago?'

'Stop it.'

'What?'

'Chatting away. Trying to make me feel better. It won't work.'

'There are two of us in this car. Guess what, Bede, maybe it makes *me* feel better. You know why I was thinking of Halbury show?'

'No idea.'

'I was wondering why you'd got that thumb-stick out.'

She was surprised at the effect her words had. He sat up and turned to her.

'Shit, Elin. I'd forgotten all about it. You're a star – that could make all the difference.' Before she could reply, he'd slumped back. 'Oh, forget it.'

'Bede, please. What?'

'No one's any more likely to believe I used that on the night of the fire than that someone broke into our house and stole a set of shoes and clothes along with the spare Bridge Farm key. Moved my glasses around, messed with my phone.'

'You used that stick? But the crutch marks are one of the things they've got against you.'

'A post-concussion hallucination, probably. Like the shadow on the yard I saw as I got home from my walk.' The beat of the wipers punctuated the pause. 'What does it matter anyway? No one's ever going to believe me.'

'They've got to.' Exasperation flooded her voice.

'Why? Even I can see which is the most convincing explanation.'

He continued staring out of the window.

'There,' he said suddenly. 'That was lightning. Happy now?'

Driving down Foxover High Street, Elin saw signs of activity as people again prepared the flood defences. It was frustrating to be unable to stop and help because of the bail conditions. She said nothing; Bede didn't need reminding. As they passed the entrance to Bridge Farm, he shifted his leg with the parasitic tagging device clinging to the ankle, sucking away at his freedom, and shrank down into his seat. It was a relief when they pulled into the Alderleat yard.

He got out and stood, arms outstretched, in the middle of the yard, face upturned to the rain. As if on cue, a flash of lightning captured the scene in a silver still. He turned to her, hair dripping.

'I think the leat could overflow this time.' He turned away and yelled out into the sodden air, 'You were right, Joe, just a year and a half too early!'

Without looking at her, he limped indoors. She noticed

he'd left the crutches in the car. Once inside, he flopped onto the sofa.

'Come on, we should start moving stuff upstairs to safety.' Elin grabbed an armful of books and photo albums from the shelves. He sat motionless, head thrown back, eyes shut.

'Stir yourself,' she insisted. 'If you think it's going to flood we need to shift as much as we can.'

'Perhaps it won't.' He opened his eyes and looked at her.

'Oh, do what you like. I am.'

He eventually joined her, unplugging and moving electrical equipment, passing things to her, insisting it was only to keep her happy. She came downstairs after taking the rolled-up rug to safety and saw him go through to the kitchen. Elin sighed, thinking of everything in the base cupboards that would need stacking on higher surfaces.

Before she could follow him, Bede returned and sat down. 'Take a good look.' He waved a hand around the bare room, then held up the kitchen scissors in the other. 'Time for a change.' He grasped a thick lock of still-damp hair and hacked it off.

She moved towards him. 'What are you doing?'

'Got to go.'

He snipped off another chunk, rubbed it dry between his fingers and let it fall to the quarry-tiled floor. She grabbed the scissors.

'Careful,' he said, beckoning for her to give them back. She refused. 'Have it your own way. I'll finish later.'

He leaned forward, swept up the blond strands and held them out to her. 'Sorry, should have thought. Take it upstairs, find a box. In memory of the man who was.'

She folded her arms in exasperation.

'No? Throw it to the river or bury it here, in Alderleat

soil.' He opened his fingers, watched the hair drift to the floor like spider's silk. 'Alderleat soil. I like that.'

'What the hell's this about?'

He stood to face her, put a hand to his head and held out another fistful of hair. 'When I was a kid, Joe asked me why didn't I get it cut for a quiet life. Now, all these years later, I can see he had a point. If I want an ounce of *respect* round here.' He spat the word. 'I'm sick of life being all about battles.'

'And this?' He flinched and Elin realised how vehemently she jabbed her finger at his chest. 'Do you intend to flay yourself?'

He reached up a hand and rubbed his neck as though the tendrils at his collar were real. 'I don't know how you can say that.'

'And I don't know how you can think about appearances at a time like this.'

He laughed incredulously. 'Appearances are everything!' He gestured at his tagged ankle. 'People are so ready to judge! Our whole world's threatened by Northcote and his fracking consortium, yet simply by standing up to it we lay ourselves open to violence from one side and malicious suspicion from the other.'

'Bede, you can't—'

'I don't know what's going on round here, but whatever it is, the blame keeps landing at my feet.' He twisted a lock of hair round his finger and held it up to her, miming scissors with his free hand. 'The kind of guy who'd burn an old lady in her home. Drown his own dog. Assault the young girl next door.'

'What?'

'Hasn't been thrown at me yet, but I dare say it's on its way.'

'Oh, for God's sake. Enough!'

'Don't you think I've had enough? Enough of threats and protesting against threats and suspicion and keeping up and trying to find new ways that it turns out aren't really any different, and…and not being able to see through it all and find the *right* way because everyone's against me and it's just one big fucking fight!'

His shoulders heaved as if every word had been a physical effort. She felt stung, as though he was including her in 'everyone'.

'I'm standing by you, aren't I?'

'And I appreciate that.'

'Try sounding as if you mean it,' she muttered as she turned towards the kitchen. With a clatter, she shoved the scissors to the back of the cutlery drawer. She took a deep breath and looked through to the living room. He was motionless on the sofa, head bowed. 'Bede. I'm sick of arguing.'

'So am I.'

The bitterness and accusation in his voice – as if she were the one picking a fight – tipped her over the edge. She got her coat from the hook.

'I'm going out before the bridge gets cut off. The river's rising and they need help in the village.' She held up a hand to silence his protest. 'Sorry if that's rubbing it in. I won't be long. You finish off in here. See if you can shed some of the self-pity by the time I get back, hey?'

She left before he could talk her out of it.

On her way to the village, his last words to her, *Be careful, El,* echoed in her mind, triggering a twinge of guilt. In the gathering dusk, she could see the gleam of the water laid out shroud-like over the fields, the flickering of the river beyond. He had a point. Maybe she was wrong to be doing this. But she needed to get away, she wouldn't be long and he might be in a better mood by the time she got back.

They were finishing off at the shop and she helped them erect the flood barriers across the entrance, then went to see what she could do for Brian and Angie in the pub. The forest of chairs stacked on tables was much the same as it had been before the floods eighteen months ago, except the lights were still on. She found them upstairs having a cup of tea with Tamsin, who was waiting for Kate.

'I tried to call you,' she said. 'See if you could pick me up on your way home.'

Elin looked at her phone. 'Sorry. I put it on silent at the police station.'

They asked after Bede. She simply said he was home and she ought to be getting back to him before long. She realised how much she wanted to.

'We've missed Eco,' Brian said. 'I hope we'll be seeing him back in the Horseshoes again soon.' Whether it was belief in his innocence or forgiveness, Elin felt a flush of warmth and wished Bede could have heard him. 'Anyway, we've had a bit of excitement of our own,' Brian continued.

'Sorry I couldn't be here. Anything I can do now?'

'You're fine, thanks. I don't mean the flooding – we've got everything more or less under control. But Tamsin's got something to tell you.'

He turned to the girl. She stared at her hands.

'It might be important, dunno.'

Elin sat down. 'What is it?'

'Silvan had Joe's diary, see. It just wasn't right; I knew the moment I saw it and—'

'Whoa, steady,' Elin said. 'What diary?'

She listened, glancing at Brian and Angie every now and then, as Tamsin told them what had happened and recounted all she could remember of the snippets she'd seen, along with Silvan's scrawled comments. 'Fires. Cars. Family. It could be my imagination, but it was, like, echoes of stuff that's been going on.' She shook her head. 'He was so weird about it. And when I said I wanted it to give to you, it was like something just snapped.'

Elin tried to grasp the significance. 'Where's Silvan now?'

'Dunno. He wanted me to go back to his place with him. But I was like, no way. He was really scary.' She looked at Brian. 'You were a star, bringing me in here. As soon as Silvan realised I wasn't going back with him, he legged it.'

She shuddered. There was a fragility about her that Elin hadn't seen before.

'What if it was him? The fire?' Tamsin said. 'And the rest – why would he do that?'

Brian got up and went to stand by the hearth. 'We called the police; they're on their way. I hope you don't mind.'

'Why would I mind?'

Elin hardly heard him as he said they didn't want to make things worse for Bede or her. An idea hovered on the edge of her mind, slow to form as she was distracted by the image of Bede at home on his own, in a state. Before hurrying back to join him, she needed to be sure.

'Tamsin, have you got a photo of Silvan on your phone?'

'Sure. Why?'

Elin was reluctant to voice her thoughts in case she was wrong. 'Send it to mine. Quick.'

Tamsin tapped on her screen as Elin searched for a number, then dialled.

'Elin Sherwell here,' she said into the mobile. 'Sorry to call out of the blue. I'm just making sure you're there – I'll explain later. I'm about to send you something. Please will you let me know straight away?'

She didn't have to wait long. A deep unease rose in her as she showed the others the photo caption: Is this your Niall?

And Suzanne Sherwell's reply: Yes, that's him. Where is he? Is he OK?

Riverflow

Elin's departure left a void that Bede wanted to fill by jumping on his bike and racing after her. No use; it would only make matters worse if he broke the terms of his injunction when they'd just got home. Resentment rose in him at the extent of the bail restrictions, and at all the wasted journeys he'd have to make to report in to the distant police station. He suppressed it, thinking of Elin's parting shot. Self-pity.

He busied himself clearing the kitchen cupboards, all the while running a variety of apologies through his mind. It was impossible to turn back the last few weeks and undo all that had happened, but he could do his damnedest to straighten things out, make it right between the two of them. He wished she'd stayed, wished he'd shown more gratitude, wished he hadn't driven her away – again. He told himself not to over-react; he'd have gone himself to help out in the village if he'd been able. Rain spattered against the window. Why did she have to go out in this, though? He thought of the day they lost Joe and suddenly none of the hurt and betrayal was important any more.

A knock at the door startled him out of his thoughts. He ignored it. No one but Elin mattered. It came again. He steeled himself, and was surprised to see Silvan dripping on the doorstep.

'You'd better come in.'

He'd never seen him so agitated.

'Glad you're back home. Shit, man, what's happened to your hair?'

Bede waved a hand in dismissal.

'Mate, I need your help,' Silvan said, hovering by the door. 'I'll explain on the way.'

'I'm not going anywhere.'

With a despairing sigh, Silvan moved to lean against the kitchen counter. 'You've got to come. You won't believe what I've seen. We can't miss this opportunity.'

'We?' Bede shook his head. 'Explain.'

Silvan told him he'd been in Holtwood making sure the pens and shoot equipment were reasonably safe from the rising water, when he'd seen lights and movement in the fields beyond.

'Drilling equipment. They're moving in.'

'Bollocks,' Bede said. 'It's ages before the appeal hearing.'

'Do you think that'd stop them? Listen, if they get as much stuff as they can in now, then when they're given the go-ahead—'

'If.'

'*If* they do, they'll have it all there ready. One protest less to face. Don't you see?'

'But it's dusk, pissing down, and the river's bursting its banks. No one in their right mind—'

'They're not in their right minds, are they?' Silvan circled a finger around his temple. 'But that's the point. No one's going to notice, or if they do, they're too preoccupied with the floods to do anything.'

'And Northcote's too preoccupied with Marjorie. Even he—'

'It's not just him, is it? The Prospect G guys could be acting off their own bat. Right now!'

Bede really didn't need this. 'What do you expect me to do about it?'

'You know.' Silvan waved a hand. 'You used to do all

that…stuff, didn't you? Monkeywrenching. Mechanical sabotage. At that protest camp of yours, Calsthorpe Wood.'

'All in the past. Anyway, where'd you hear about that?'

Silvan hesitated. 'Tammy told me. Elin told her.' He moved impatiently towards the door. 'Fuck's sake man, will you stop wasting time?'

It might be in the past, but the memory of Calsthorpe stirred a familiar anger. Bede had never truly believed Northcote would go ahead with this. Before he could get swept along on a tide of rage, an imaginary tingle spread from the tag on his ankle. 'I'm not allowed more than a mile radius from the house. That puts the far side of Holtwood and anything beyond it out of bounds.'

'Jesus H Christ! What kind of activist are you? What you said – it's nearly dark and it's pissing down. You'll be home before anyone knows.'

'What's dark got to do with it?' Bede tapped his leg. 'Either this thing's waterproof and keeps spying on me or it goes dead and they know I'm up to something. Whichever, I'm not risking—'

'All right, we don't set foot beyond the woods. Have you got a decent camera? We collect some evidence, then it's up to you – and Elin – what you do with it.'

Bede thought of Elin's disillusionment at his refusal to get more involved. If he acted now, for her, surely it would beat any of the apologies he'd just been rehearsing. Actions speaking louder than words and all that. He stood. Silvan shuffled from foot to foot by the door as he went through to the living room to get his camera, and sighed with impatience as Bede opened the bag and checked it over, put on his coat, tucked his glasses in his pocket and grabbed his walking stick.

'At last.' Silvan headed out to the jeep.

Bede was about to lock up and follow when his eyes fell on the phone. He quickly dialled Elin's mobile, swore as the recorded message told him she was on another call, and left a voicemail. 'There's stuff happening beyond Holtwood. I'm going to check out what we can do about it. I'll be back soon. Love you.'

Plumes of water arced to either side of the jeep as Silvan sped down the lane, clearly enjoying the drama. 'They'll have accessed the site round the back roads, of course,' he said, 'but we'll head this way. Don't want to get you into any more trouble.'

The Holtwood track was too churned up for them to go far.

'We'll have to walk from here.' He parked out of sight of the road. Bede levered himself from the car, a twinge from his healing ankle making him wonder what on earth he was doing here. He looked down the short, steep bank at the river sliding past, menacingly close. The dusky air was still saturated; a light rain fell, punctuated by fatter splashes from the dripping leaves. He peered through the trees.

'I can't see any lights.'

'They must've left the stuff and gone.'

'What, no security lights?'

'Who d'you think I am?' Silvan looked at him for a moment in the half-light, before breaking into a smile. 'I'm Northcote's gamekeeper, not his security guard.'

'I don't know what sort of pictures you expect me to get in these conditions.' He handed the bulky camera bag to Silvan. 'Carry this for me, will you?'

Silvan shouldered the bag and trudged along the track. Bede followed, bracing himself with the walking stick, stumbling in the slippery ruts, the waterlogged ground soaking his feet. They came to a point where the river had filled a dip in the ground to form a lagoon barring their way. Silvan stopped; Bede caught him up and stood beside him. He was momentarily distracted by the constantly changing patterns of the water as it hurried past the fringe of trees where he'd brought Elin the first time she came to Foxover. This time there was a clear meaning in the water's voice – he understood the warning. Wishing he hadn't come, he reminded himself he was doing this for her.

'We'd better get moving,' he said. 'We'll have to go round.'

He turned to skirt the water. Silvan put a hand on his arm.

'No. Looks like this is the end.'

Bede shuddered. Something about that voice. 'We've come this far.' He hoped she'd appreciate this. 'No point giving up now.'

'Oh, I think we've gone far enough.' Silvan smiled faintly through the gathering gloom. 'How far do I have to go before you realise?'

The voice again; his accent was different – like Joe's. As Bede stared, he spoke again.

'There is no illegal site invasion, *cousin*.'

With all pretence gone, despite the wet hair plastered to his forehead and the mocking contempt on his face, there was a hint of family Bede was shocked not to have seen before. 'Hang on. You're Niall? Joe's Niall?'

He clapped his hands slowly. 'Congratulations. So now you know. All the things we have in common.' He glanced down towards Bede's ankle then back up to meet his eyes. 'What we're driven to.'

His voice was raised slightly above the sounds of wind and water.

'Couldn't we have had this conversation at home?'

Niall laughed and Bede felt afraid. This was merely the latest in a long line of scheming. So much cold, calculating effort. Taking a few steps back, Bede drew courage from the rushing of the river and daggers of rain that stirred up his anger.

'Why didn't you just tell us who you were?'

'What good would that have done?'

'We could have—'

'Could've what? Shared Alderleat with me?' He let out a spiteful laugh. 'You had your chance. I was ready to...to let it all drop. But you made it quite clear where you were coming from, didn't you?'

'If you'd—'

Growing rage and a rain-heavy gust cut him short.

'What would I want with that old relic anyway? I just wanted to get to you.' He shook his head in sham concern. 'Never intended you to get hurt that badly, though.'

Bede laughed incredulously.

'Sorry,' Niall said. 'You just have a way of pushing my buttons.'

'It wasn't only me, though, was it? What about Elin?'

'Oh, yes she pushed my buttons all right.' Niall splashed across the boggy ground towards him. 'Different ones.'

Bede continued to edge back. He's lying. Don't let the bastard get to you.

'Come on, be honest with me. If you could have Joe back, if your dad was somehow here, wouldn't you feel the same? Wouldn't you want to give them hell?'

'No.' Bede's knuckles were white on his stick. 'No, I wouldn't. Not like this.'

''Course not. You're some kind of saint, aren't you? Squeaky clean. You can justify everything. Even conspiring to con your place out of Marjorie Northcote.'

'You what? We—'

'You paid for it fair and square. Didn't you? So why was Joe rubbing his hands with glee in his diary?'

'What diary?'

A smile spread across Niall's face.

'Kept that from you too, did he? What a pity. You'd have enjoyed reading it. He worshipped you, you know. A shame you didn't find it before I did. Could've saved you so much trouble, so much heartache.' He reached in his pocket and held up a set of keys, the familiar metal J of the key-ring making Bede's heart lurch. 'You should've been more observant. I watched him stash it away. The day he stayed behind to save his precious things from the flood.'

A flicker of movement in the willows. Joe's death no accident.

'That…that was you?'

Niall looked back at him with an insolent grin. He raised his arm and threw the keys into the water. As they hit the surface, the dam of Bede's rage finally broke. He splashed forward, clutched the walking stick and lunged at him. Niall dodged and yanked it from him. Betrayed by his weakened wrist, Bede let go too easily.

Elin stared out of the window as she finished the call. It hadn't been easy to explain about Niall to Suzanne Sherwell; she'd been as tactful as she could and promised to call back later when they knew more. Outside, the water was rising and it looked like the bridge would be cut off soon. She looked round at the others in Brian and Angie's flat.

'I'm not waiting any longer. I've got to get home to Bede. Tell the police to come and find us there.'

As she tucked her phone away, she noticed a missed call. His voicemail message took a moment to register. Mystified, she turned back to the window and looked at the wind-buffeted silhouette of Holtwood's trees beyond the river. 'Stuff happening'? As she expected, she could see no signs of life. Her mind was still racing with the implications of Silvan's identity, and she felt there must be some connection.

With Tamsin sitting in uncharacteristic silence beside her, she drove over the bridge and eased the car through the growing lake on the far side. She pictured Bede looking up at her from the sofa as she got back to the house. Whatever his mood, she had never wished more fervently for him to be there.

Her fears were confirmed by the empty house. She managed to persuade Tamsin to stay, lock the door and phone the pub to tell them Elin was heading for Holtwood. As she approached the entrance to the forestry track, she saw headlights cross the bridge from the village and a car cautiously negotiate the floodwater blanketing the road. She recognised the detective's car and felt a sudden stab of doubt. The last thing they needed was to get Bede into deeper trouble. He shouldn't risk being in Holtwood, and if the message meant what she thought it did, he shouldn't be doing what he was doing. But his safety was more important than any of it.

She turned into the woods and her breath caught as she saw the shoot jeep racing towards her, lights blazing. Stuck in the muddy ruts, she had nowhere to go. All she could do was brake and brace herself. The jeep swerved, then seemed to be caught up by some invisible hand and tugged forcefully down the slope towards the river. Saplings bent, undergrowth was crushed beneath its slide. It glanced off a tree and slipped backwards towards the water's edge.

Elin was out of her car in an instant, watching in horror as the river clawed at the jeep with strong fingers of current. Silvan – Niall – managed to scramble out, but she didn't care as she peered at the passenger seat – empty but for a camera bag – and the half-submerged rear compartment. Niall was scrambling up the bank, sliding back towards the flood with each step.

'Where's Bede?' she yelled.

He paused, clinging to a branch, and looked up at her with a mocking half-smile.

'Tell me!' She wanted to rain every curse she knew down on him. 'What have you *done*?'

'Me? That's rich! He's gone mad—' His foot slipped and he reached out. She made no move. 'You're both fucking mad!'

Before she could think whether or not to help, Elin heard car doors slam and glanced round to see Inspector Hughes and a colleague. Niall had grasped a fistful of undergrowth and clung on as the jeep sank slowly into the water behind him. Let the police deal with him. Elin stumbled as fast as she could along the track in the direction he'd come from. The churned ruts hampered her feet. She lost a boot in the mud. It barely registered. All she wanted was to find Bede.

The pattering rain was as relentless as her conscience. She'd driven him here.

A breeze rustled the leaves as she was cut off by an expanse of floodwater. Her heart was in her mouth as she recognised the place, weirdly changed. Bede's walking stick floated in an eddy pool. Numbly, she splashed her way out and grasped it, leaning on it as she looked around.

Then she saw him. Clinging one-handed to a low branch, he floated with the water lapping at his bruised face, hair pooling around him, body rocking to and fro in the rising current. Elin stared at him in horror. She called out. He turned his head slightly and their eyes met as a gust of wind swayed the tree and a surge of water jostled him. He let go, floundering weakly, then went under. Spurred into action, she waded over, grasped a branch to anchor herself and managed to grab his coat. She dragged him out, to ground that was sodden but out of the grip of the riverflow.

He was deathly pale. Heedless of the cold and wet, she knelt and hugged his freezing, motionless body to her. She shouted into the trees, unable to leave him and trusting help would come. She rubbed his arms, his shoulders, desperately trying to share her body warmth, as he coughed the river from his lungs. He huddled up to her and she gripped his hand. He squeezed hers weakly.

'What the hell were you doing here?' The reprimand slipped out in a heady mix of panic and relief.

'He…he lied to me. He said that Northcote… I thought you'd want me to… Oh, I'll tell you later.'

Elin heard the sound of vehicles and distant shouts. It was all faint beneath the roar of the river, but she thought she could make out Brian; Tamsin, even. Hadn't she told her to stay safe at Alderleat? Bede was shivering violently. She shifted. 'We should move. Can you stand?'

Clutching her for support, he braced himself, then inhaled sharply. 'No good. Bastard smashed my ankle.' He slumped against her. 'Again.'

'Again?'

'I'm sure it was him who… You won't believe who he is, El.'

'I know.'

She regretted the words as she said them.

'You knew?'

'Only about half an hour—'

'Stop. Don't explain. No need. We'll deal with him…' He looked out over the fast-flowing floodwater. 'With all of it…together. He doesn't matter. We matter.'

It was too cloudy for moonlight but as she followed his gaze, the river looked and sounded different.

So I've decided to write a few things down, like my old dad did. Weird I should even think of doing anything like that bastard. But how many times have I read him blathering about how it helped him, so maybe it'll help me. Not that I regret what happened. Wasn't my fault was it? He provoked me. Almost as if he expected it. Wanted it?? Stupid sod, what do I care?

I was prompted to put pen to paper by this letter Bede sent me. Couldn't believe it, after all these months, years even. He actually thanked me!! Not for the companionship & good times when he was laid up, or anything like that (though I guess I can hardly blame him when it was me put him there in the first place), but for "providing the circumstances that finally helped me see where I'd been going wrong". I seriously wonder what planet he's on.

Thanked me! As if he'd forgotten how I made things as difficult as I could for him - my word against his & all that. Activist breaking the terms of his bail versus helpful mate trying to make him see sense? It might even have worked too, if someone hadn't (at last, congrats!!) thought to check the gig I was supposed to have been at when he was knocked off his bike. It all slid from there, sympathy shifted his way, & the publicity - which he claimed not to want! - even pushed the remaining fence-sitters in the village & beyond into the arms of their little Frack-Free Foxover clan.

Helped by old Marjorie recovering a bit & making her opinion known.

Said he'd been prompted to send an olive branch – was he trying to be clever or what? Call me Noah ha ha – after the birth of their child. Do I give a fuck? They called her Hope, as if that'll bring some answers.

Can't see what's so special about answers myself, though I've thought a lot about why I hated my big gawky cousin so much. It certainly wasn't because I wanted anything he had.

Revenge – that old classic? But why? What did he ever do to me? Who knows. I've had the words 'cold & calculating' thrown at me often enough, but in truth it just came over me as I kept reading about the mutual fan club in the old man's diary, & I wanted to hurt him, & hurt her because that was another way of getting to him, & once it got me in its grip...well, it was just part of the game.

Maybe that's all it was. A game. A way of passing the time.

I still can't believe it was that easy. So they'd been through a bad patch, but even so. They're both intelligent people & you'd think they'd be sharper than that. Honestly, what chance have they got of finding their place in the world? They'll just keep getting walked all over – no more than they deserve.

Though maybe I'm being unfair. After all, they're there & I'm cut off from it all in here.

Acknowledgements

I am grateful as ever to all at Honno, especially Caroline Oakley and Helena Earnshaw, for their belief in my writing and hard work on my behalf.

I am indebted to the Hawthornden Foundation, and the late Drue Heinz, for the month I spent writing the second half of this novel at the beautiful and inspiring Hawthornden castle.

Special thanks to my friends Martine Bailey and Elaine Walker for invaluable feedback, insight and support at all stages of writing this novel and beyond. I would also like to thank my early readers, John Maskall, Clare Smith, Ann Stonehouse, John Stonestreet, Karen Johnson, Ed Layland, Trina Layland, Natalie Lloyd and James Layland, for their insights, comments and encouragement. Thanks to the Prime Writers and the family of Honno authors for long-standing friendship and support.

Ali Rashidbaigi provided helpful advice on the medical treatment of fractures and concussion. Any errors are, of course, all mine.

My gratitude to Richard Bentley for in-depth information and fascinating conversations about floods, water mills and all things riparian. Again, any errors are mine; I should note here that this is a work of fiction, and the last time this part of Shropshire was subject to the kind of spring rain and summer floods described in the novel was in 2007, although climate change means similar freak conditions are ever more likely. I have also moved the zone threatened by fracking a number of miles south towards the Severn and the fictional location of Foxover.

Last but not least, I give my heartfelt thanks to my family, especially my husband David, for everything.

ABOUT HONNO

Honno Welsh Women's Press was set up in 1986 by a group of women who felt strongly that women in Wales needed wider opportunities to see their writing in print and to become involved in the publishing process. Our aim is to develop the writing talents of women in Wales, give them new and exciting opportunities to see their work published and often to give them their first 'break' as a writer. Honno is registered as a community co-operative. Any profit that Honno makes is invested in the publishing programme. Women from Wales and around the world have expressed their support for Honno. Each supporter has a vote at the Annual General Meeting. For more information and to buy our publications, please write to Honno at the address below, or visit our website: www.honno.co.uk

Honno, 14 Creative Units, Aberystwyth Arts Centre,
Aberystwyth, Ceredigion SY23 3GL

Honno Friends

We are very grateful for the support
of the Honno Friends:
Jane Aaron, Gwyneth Tyson Roberts, Beryl Thomas

For more information on how you can support Honno,
see: https://www.honno.co.uk/about/support-honno/